"Good mor...

Bryce's voice wa... ...and husky as Sarah joined him on his private balcony. "I watched you sleeping and decided that if I didn't get up, I'd have to wake you," he added. He smiled suggestively, making sure his meaning was very clear.

Sarah's smile was deliberately enticing as she nestled into his strong lean arms. "I'm awake now," she murmured, her heart filled with a love she had never thought possible.

Reaching inside her red silk robe, Bryce ran his hands slowly across her bare back. His gentle mouth moved down on hers. At first his kiss was tender, then it grew passionate. Against her trembling lips he whispered, "Since you are awake, let's go back to bed. . . ."

Dear Reader,

So, you couldn't resist Temptation! Small wonder—we couldn't either. In fact, we got so excited about these new books that we decided to publish them under the prestigious Mills & Boon imprint.

Of course, we trust you will continue to love your other Mills & Boon books; those heart-warming, uplifting romances millions of women all over the world have enjoyed for so long. Temptation is a new choice, above all for those who like a good, passionate, sensual read.

As with everything we publish, you, dear reader, are the judge. And you can help us tremendously with comments and suggestions for Temptation. Why don't you drop me a line?

Linda

The Editor
Temptation
Mills & Boon Ltd
15–16 Brook's Mews
London W1A 1DR

Friend of the Heart

DIANNE KING

MILLS & BOON LIMITED
15–16 BROOK'S MEWS
LONDON W1A 1DR

First published in Great Britain in 1985 by Mills & Boon Limited, 15–16 Brook's Mews, London W1A 1DR

© Dianne King 1984

ISBN 0 263 75147 3

21–0685

Printed and bound in Great Britain by Cox & Wyman Ltd, Reading

1

SARAH MONTGOMERY HURRIED OUT of the BART station and up Powell Street. It was midmorning, mid-August, and San Francisco was at its finest. A brisk breeze blew off the bay and the sunlit blue sky was completely free of low coastal clouds. This Friday was an extraordinary day. Unable to contain her joie de vivre, Sarah smiled indiscriminately at pass-ersby. She'd just signed the best contract yet for Montgomery Advertising—a new logo, brochures and stationery for Bay Radio and TV. She couldn't wait to get back to the office to share her good news.

As she waited for the light to change, she stepped to the sidewalk flower stand. White, yellow and pink daisies, bunches of violets, bouquets of red carna-tions and chrysanthemums of all varieties made it difficult to choose. Quickly, she settled for a huge pom-pom chrysanthemum in bronze and gold.

"No," she said, resisting the vendor's urging. "I only want one."

Counting out her change, the old gentleman made a mock bow. "A pretty posy for a pretty lady," he said with a broad smile. "'N have a nice day...as the young people say."

"I will...I *am*." Sarah smiled her thanks and turned down Geary. With the flower in her hand, she was a sight as bright as the day—a smartly dressed, slender young woman. Her long honey-colored hair hung thick and straight past her shoulders. Her

golden-brown eyes sparkled with excitement and
her cheeks were flushed a rosy hue from her brisk
walk.

San Franciscans always walked everywhere...
John had said that, Sarah remembered. She lowered
her head to sniff the piquant fragrance of the chrysanthemum and thought about John.

John Carr, only thirty-three and a rising young
star of Hansen and Carr, Architects. Robb Hansen,
an engineer, and John, the creative designer, were a
dynamite combination. Last year their firm had
landed a lucrative contract designing plants for a
multinational computer company. Hansen, in his
early forties and a family man, was glad that John
was single and enjoyed traveling.

John was also charming and handsome, Sarah
told herself, and had been in Stuttgart for the past
three weeks. Before that, he'd been home one week
after having been in Hawaii for two weeks. All in all,
he'd been gone from San Francisco much more than
he'd been here the entire summer.

But he would be home Monday, and he would be
delighted with her new contract. And proud of her.
She could count on a wonderful celebration, John
would make it so. He loved an excuse for a party.

They'd been invited to one this evening at socialite
Bebe McDonald's. After almost two years, people invited them as a couple. It had been at such a party as
tonight's that she'd met tall dark-haired John. He
had designed the palatial Hillsborough home and
every unattached woman at the party had been interested in him. But men liked him too and that
pleased Sarah. John was urbane and witty. He was
not yet rich, but he was very ambitious and immensely talented. That night Sarah had observed he
received his well-deserved accolades for the house
modestly. Charmingly modest, she knew now.

When he'd singled her out, she'd felt like Cinderella at the ball. Certainly he was Prince Charming.

Once more she thought how pleased he would be about her new contract and wished she could tell him about it right now. After all, he'd encouraged her to start her own advertising firm.

Sarah hurried through Union Square, dodging a flurry of pigeons settling in an iridescent swirl of gray and white to gather cookie crumbs a trio of exuberant youngsters were tossing onto the sidewalk. Without breaking her stride, she managed to side-step a tourist who stopped suddenly to consult a guidebook. Passing the one-hundred-plus-year-old I. Magnin's and the new glass-fronted Neiman-Marcus, she turned up Stockton Street. She glanced up at the ornate old-fashioned facade of the building that housed her office. John often teased her about it, disdainfully comparing it to his ultramodern one in the prestigious One Embarcadero Center building. Pushing open the heavy glass door, she hurried to the waiting elevator.

As she entered her office, her secretary-receptionist looked up from her typewriter. "Good morning, Miss Montgomery."

When Lara greeted her this way, Sarah knew clients were present. She glanced at the man sitting in the corner with a newspaper obscuring his face.

"Did we get the contract?" Lara whispered as Sarah laid the portfolio on the desk.

"We did. Give this to Joan so she can place orders for space and printing, okay? And here's a posy for you."

"Terrific!" Lara's smile deepened the dimples that belied the sophisticated image she tried for. Behind oversized glasses her pale blue eyes widened with joy.

Sarah loved the loyalty that made Lara say "we."

She knew it stemmed from Lara's sense of gratitude. She was barely twenty-one, just out of business college, when Sarah took a chance on her. Sarah was both amused and flattered at the way Lara looked up to her. According to Lara, Sarah had it made. A *terrific* career and John Carr.

At Lara's excited response, the man looked questioningly over his newspaper. "Mr. Benedict's been waiting to see you." She lowered her voice. "Grant Holcomb referred him."

How odd, Sarah thought. Grant was an account executive with one of the biggest advertising firms in the city. Although they were friends, she couldn't imagine why he would steer a client away from his own agency.

Well, she told herself, *never look a gift horse in the mouth.*

"Sorry to keep you waiting, Mr. Benedict," she said, walking over to him and extending her hand.

He rose from the chair, a tall man whose presence suddenly seemed to fill the small reception room. A Harris-tweed jacket fit his broad shoulders with well tailored ease. Quickly Sarah took in his sun-streaked light brown hair, his tanned face with its aquiline nose and firm mouth. But what arrested her attention were his eyes—they were a changeable mixture of green, gold and brown, and at the moment they were glinting angrily.

Pulling herself away from that furious forceful gaze, she realized with a small shock that the hand gripping hers was hard. The hand of a workingman, she thought. For an instant, she remembered John's hands, uncalloused, sensitive and always well manicured. She noted that this man's nails were well manicured too. She hoped the anger in his eyes was not due to her late arrival.

As they went into Sarah's private office, Benedict

ignored the oak-and-glass furniture and the tall window that overlooked Union Square.

Planting himself squarely in front of Sarah's desk, he began without preamble, "I've just fired Grant Holcomb and that asinine agency he works for. He suggested your agency might suit me better, and since I have no idea where else to go, I've come here."

Sarah was taken aback by the man's straightforward manner. He would be an extremely demanding client. She wondered what kind of scene had just taken place between him and Grant.

"Well, that's very kind of Grant," Sarah finally managed to respond, sitting down behind her desk. "Won't you take a seat, Mr. Benedict?"

Ignoring her invitation, he continued, "I've been working with Holcomb for months. He couldn't possibly have misunderstood! Such incompetence is hard for me to—" He broke off and made a visible effort to regain his composure. He gave a wry smile that did nothing to soften the anger reflected in his eyes, then shrugged. "Well, he said you have a good eye and excellent taste. Which obviously is something his agency lacks."

He paused, taking in her beige natural-linen suit and ivory silk blouse. Sarah saw his eyes linger on the simple yet stunning pearls John had brought her from Hong Kong. For the first time, he seemed to relax slightly.

"I can see he was right," he finished.

"Why don't you tell me exactly what you'd like me to do for you," she suggested in a tone much less relaxed than she normally used with clients. "And, please, won't you sit down."

"I own Benedict Winery out in the Valley of the Moon. Have you heard of it?" he asked, finally taking the chair opposite her.

Thank goodness, she had, Sarah thought. "Yes. Your winery produces my favorite Chardonnay. Unfortunately I can only afford it for special occasions."

At last he smiled. White even teeth flashed in his suntanned face, squint lines crinkled at the corners of his eyes. And something Sarah couldn't quite identify—a sensitivity, a vulnerability—showed for the briefest moment.

Inexplicably, Sarah felt her pulse quicken as his eyes held hers.

"Holcomb's firm was to do the campaign for a sparkling red wine I'm introducing this fall. It's a relatively inexpensive wine, my first attempt to crack the mass market. Holcomb presented their campaign to me an hour ago."

Once more she saw gold fire glint in his eyes as he continued angrily. "Obviously they weren't listening when I explained what I wanted. This wine isn't expensive. But the label they proposed looked like it belonged on soda pop!"

He slammed his strong hands on the surface of her desk. "Something's really amiss at that agency. When I began considering this advertising campaign, I interviewed several firms. Holcomb's seemed compatible with my philosophy. We've certainly had enough meetings. Been at this *for months.* I still can't believe what they put together for this final conference." Removing his hands from her desk, he sat back in his chair in an obvious attempt at self-control.

After a moment, he smiled apologetically at Sarah. "Enough of this ranting and raving. Holcomb said if I want something simple and elegant, you could do it. Can you? In two months? That's all the time there is left."

Two months, Sarah thought. That wasn't time enough to set up an entire ad campaign.

"The magazine and newspaper space has already been contracted for," Benedict added. "Holcomb did do something right, I guess."

"And time for radio? TV?" Sarah could see that he knew what was involved. And that was good.

"Yes. A TV commercial film crew's been hired. The mechanics of their campaign was not what I objected to. It was their philosophy. Do you think you might be interested?"

Sarah pressed the intercom button. "Lara, bring in the Saratoga Sparkling Water file, please." Looking directly at Benedict, she went on, "I think you should see some of my work before we go any further."

He nodded, then leaned back in the chair, finally letting the long length of his body relax.

It's ridiculous, Sarah thought, to feel so physically aware of this man. And yet, he's so...commanding.

Lara entered, laying the file on Sarah's desk. "Mr. Carr's on the phone," she said, then left.

Sarah handed the file to Benedict, then picked up the phone. She turned slightly in her chair so that she wasn't directly facing the man as she talked.

"Sarah." John's pleasant voice came over the line. "How's my lady? I've missed you."

"How are things in Stuttgart?" she asked, aware that Benedict glanced up at her, then returned to his examination of the file.

"I said, I've missed you," John repeated, then waited for her reply.

"Well, yes. You must remember that you're on West German time. We aren't even to lunchtime yet," she countered, wishing John would not put her in this awkward position. He called whenever he had free time, the convenience of the hour did not concern him. "When will you be back?"

"You have a client in your office, right?"

"That's correct."

"I'll be home Monday. Sorry I couldn't make it by tonight. Be sure to give my personal regrets to Bebe, won't you?" He didn't wait for her reply, but continued, "Only three more days. We've got a lot of time to make up. Right?" he asked in a husky whisper.

Wishing she was taking this call in private, Sarah answered, "Yes. You're right." Out of the corner of her eye, she caught a look of discomfort on Benedict's face and saw him shift in his chair. She needed to terminate this conversation.

"Are you ready for Hawaii?" John asked.

Suddenly Sarah felt her heart sink. Hawaii. For the moment, she'd completely forgotten about it.

They were supposed to leave next Friday for a week in Hawaii where John was to make a supervision check on another building under construction for the computer company. If she took on the Benedict account she couldn't possibly go.

After she was silent for a long moment, John asked, "Sarah, is something wrong?"

"No...yes...I'm sorry. Can we talk when you get back? I have a client here now and I...."

"Sure, love. See you Monday. Bye."

When she hung up, she turned back to face Benedict. "Well?" she asked.

He laid the file on her desk. "This is just the kind of work I want. Holcomb knew what he was doing when he recommended you." He glanced at his watch. "If you're free, let me take you to lunch and we'll discuss it. I think we can do business."

Quickly consulting her appointment calendar, Sarah agreed, "Very well. Just give me a minute to fix my face."

He smiled. Again his entire personality changed before her eyes. The look he gave her was charmingly bold. "That face needs no fixing."

And as before, Sarah felt her pulse quicken in response to the directness of his gaze.

"How about Doro's?" he asked.

"It's Friday and without a reservation...." She paused wondering if perhaps he had a reservation.

"It'll be all right," he assured her. "Come on, let's go."

Doro's restaurant was a favorite with advertising people. As Sarah and Benedict followed the headwaiter through the softly lit room, she nodded to several acquaintances. He'd been right—the fact that he hadn't a reservation was no problem. The maître d' had greeted him by name.

When seated, Sarah looked around enjoying the classic elegance of the white tablecloths, fresh flowers and subdued atmosphere. She'd had enough excitement this morning. It was lovely to relax.

A few minutes later, a waiter took their order—shrimp Louie for Sarah and petrale sole for her host. He carefully looked over the wine list before ordering a bottle of Benedict Fumé Blanc.

"No point in false modesty," he told her with a smile, then he must have remembered her comment about the Chardonnay. "Unless you'd prefer—"

"The Fumé Blanc will do nicely," Sarah told him. That smile... it was both unexpected and fascinating, so at odds with the tenseness she'd observed in him for most of their conversation. He was obviously very annoyed with Grant Holcomb's firm. She wondered if perhaps he was angry at himself.

Sarah found herself staring at him, then abruptly looked away.

This is ridiculous, she told herself, irritated at her lack of composure. *I'm not fifteen, and this man is not the captain of the football team. He's a potential client who obviously will be difficult to please.*

"Miss Montgomery," he began, then stopped. "If

we're going to work together, first names would be more appropriate. Why don't you call me Bryce...."

His voice trailed off and suddenly Sarah realized he didn't know her name.

"Sarah," she explained.

"Mmm. With an *h* or without?"

With a wry smile, she answered, "With."

When she'd entered the University of Minnesota, she'd dropped the *h*. The same way she'd dropped religion, family and tradition. But by Christmas vacation of her sophomore year she'd recovered her equilibrium and put the *h* back in her old-fashioned name and regained some respect for the old-fashioned virtues she was raised with.

Bryce cocked a dark eyebrow quizzically. "You look like you're remembering a secret joke."

"No. Just my misspent youth," she replied dryly.

He looked critically at her. "You're not a native San Franciscan, are you?" he guessed with amazing accuracy.

"No. Don't tell me that beneath this I. Magnin suit I have Minnesota Farm Girl written all over me?"

He laughed. "In a way. You appear very sophisticated. But there's something...maybe it's a lack of...." He searched for the right word, then said, "Audacity. You weren't comfortable with that phone call you had. I was sorry to add to your discomfort."

Astonished, Sarah couldn't think of an appropriate reply, so she said nothing.

"So," he continued, "you're from Minnesota. Why did you leave?"

No pleasantries about seeking one's fortune or Minnesota's loss, San Francisco's gain. His question was direct and personal. Yet Sarah didn't mind. "The lure of the big time," she answered. "I wanted more than was available there."

To her surprise, a wary look replaced Bryce's friendliness.

I've put him off somehow, she realized, and was dismayed at how much the thought bothered her.

At that moment, the wine steward opened the bottle of Fumé Blanc and poured it with a flourish. Testing it critically, Bryce nodded. "Excellent," he said shortly.

When he filled her glass, she tasted the wine and considered its pronounced flavor. "Very nice indeed," she commented.

Picking up the bottle, he pointed out the logo. "From my grandfather's days...old-fashioned, maybe, but I won't change it. It stands for something."

Sarah scrutinized the *B* and *W* intertwined and illuminated in the medieval manner. It was graceful—the proportions exactly right. She wouldn't change it either.

Studying his wineglass, not looking at Sarah, Bryce continued in a voice tight with suppressed anger. "I've been planning the premiere of this wine since spring. Holcomb has been up to the winery and we've met here in the city. We both speak English...there's no excuse for that pop-artish presentation they made today. It was slick and trendy and totally meaningless." He shook his head. "A bunch of idiots."

Sarah realized fully why Bryce Benedict and Grant Holcomb hadn't seen eye to eye. Grant always considered the product secondary to the ad campaign. Bryce clearly didn't feel that way.

"What did they design?" she asked.

"Circles of gold with wine-red lettering," he answered with a grimace.

"A bit garish for anything selling for over a dollar a bottle."

For a moment Bryce looked at her, startled, then he smiled broadly. And with his eyes, as well.

We're back where we were a moment ago, Sarah thought. Relieved, she returned his smile.

Just then the waiter brought their lunch. As they began to eat, Bryce asked if she was at all familiar with the wine country.

"I love it," she replied. "It's one of my favorite things about living in San Francisco. I've done several of the tasting tours, but I'm not a connoisseur really. Just an aficionado."

Grinning, he picked up his glass and, in mock salute, said, "To the aficionados. *They* buy the wine."

With a smile, Sarah quickly picked up her glass to respond. As she heard the delicate chime of crystal against crystal, she studied Bryce Benedict. What had caught her attention when they'd first met were his eyes, their commingling of color and the fire of...anger? He'd made no effort to mask displeasure. Since then, she'd watched the man behind the eyes be open, then closed, open, then closed. John was mercurial, heaven knows, but this man was beginning to be downright wearing. It couldn't be anything about her. They were strangers.

Sarah's art training made her constantly aware and appreciative of light, its power and patterns. She saw and felt things in that context. The light permitted to shine through those hazel eyes came as capriciously as sunlight shafting through a bank of summer storm clouds.

There was an anger, or perhaps it was fear, banked within this man sitting across the table from her, that every now and then blanked out his friendliness. It was as if he told himself stop...back up. Something, someone, other than Grant Holcomb, had made him extremely distrustful. Once again his countenance wore a look of wariness.

The interest she'd sensed in him just minutes earlier was definitely gone. Now he looked at her as someone he was hiring to do a job. All right, she thought, and said, "Tell me about Benedict Winery."

"Well," he began, "Benedict Winery is not on tasting tours. It's third generation, family owned and controlled. It is a struggle to stay small and still survive in this very competitive business. The secret is to specialize and concentrate on excellence. Not with *vin ordinaire* but with *vin extraordinaire*. Like this," he said as he lifted his glass in mock salute, then sipped the wine.

They ate in silence for a few minutes, then as Bryce buttered a piece of bread, he continued speaking, "Before my father died five years ago, he conceived the idea of producing a sparkling red wine. He did some market research, planned and increased our acreage of Pinot Noir grapes. Most important, he insisted that the wine was to be produced by the classic *methode champenoise.*"

Sarah lifted her hand to interrupt him. "Translation, please," she said grinning at him. "Remember I told you I'm only an aficionado."

"Sorry," he apologized with a laugh. "He wanted this to be a preferred wine. Bottle fermented, not bulk processed."

Sarah nodded. Now she remembered. The best quality sparkling wines are made with the secondary fermentation occurring in the same bottle that goes to market.

"This new wine is part of his legacy to me. He spent years working out the blend. We've been producing this wine for the past three years and have sufficient inventory to market this year. My father left a vineyard, a winery, a house that he designed himself and an impeccable reputation." He went on to tell her his father had studied with Frank Lloyd

Wright and that he had made a considerable contribution to both architecture and to the wine industry in the Valley of the Moon. "I want this wine to be a credit to his name. Pop art won't do it," he finished. The anger was gone from his voice, and from his eyes.

Silently, Sarah considered his obvious sensitivity. "He must have been an unusual man," she said softly.

"He was quite extraordinary."

Clearly, there was a great deal more he could say, but he'd told her enough so that she felt she knew what he wanted for this new wine.

"We don't buy goods anymore," she explained. "They're sold to us. But there's a hard sell and a soft sell, and I believe in the latter. Quality of merchandise, product and idea should be the prime consideration of advertising art. The cost of something doesn't always determine the excellence of it. Its value—its intrinsic value—is what must be presented to capture the buyer and keep him."

"Yes, to keep him. That is important, competition being what it is. Perfect." Bryce leaned back and looked at her. "I think you'll do. If you can handle the job, it's yours."

Sarah considered this abrupt offer. "Are you telling me you want designing, printing and mailing done in two months?"

"Less, actually. I want to officially premiere the wine at the end of harvest. For us, the end of October." He added, "And, of course, I want it done right."

"Of course," she echoed with a smile. "So do I. This afternoon I'll contact some people I like to work with because I know I can count on them. I'll do the job for you." She looked at him and spoke candidly, "It hasn't been that long since I was one of the hungry firms, working on little more than hope. I haven't forgotten how to hustle."

"Good."

Finishing her salad, Sarah absently speared the last bite of shrimp. Obviously they didn't need to discuss budget. Nice way to do business. It would be a challenging project that could lead to bigger and better things. Her head was buzzing with ideas and fragments of design and copy. "Do you have a name for this new wine?" she asked.

He smiled and shrugged, lifting one hand in that age-old gesture of question. "Well, I've doodled a lot of names on a lot of notepaper. But, as yet, nothing has seemed exactly right."

One of those fragments of color and shape and sound that flitted in and out of Sarah's head took form. She saw again the Fumé Blanc being poured by the sommelier into the wineglass. And saw again, the delicate tinge of color—whether from the light or from the glass, she didn't know, but the light at least intensified the essence of color. Essence was a favorite word of Sarah's. For her, it caught the subtle qualities of what identified anything—a place, a person.

Discreetly, she studied the man seated across from her. Nicely groomed, poised and very attractive with his sun-streaked light brown hair. She judged him to be in his early-to-mid-thirties, and thought he had the kind of good looks that wear well. He'd age gracefully, and when old, be distinguished looking. He blended perfectly into this elegantly classic atmosphere. Classic, a rare breed these days, she mused.

And then it came to her. The name. "How does this sound—Benedict Vintage Recherché?"

"Recherché...." Bryce repeated thoughtfully, tasting it on his tongue as he might taste a fine wine.

"Uncommon...rare...incredible," he said, his voice rising with excitement. "It's the perfect name."

His enthusiasm made Sarah flush with pleasure.

"You've got to come up to the winery," he said, as if there could be no question of her agreement. "Tomorrow. Then you can get a feel for the place and the product before you start the ad campaign."

Tomorrow was Saturday and Sarah had plans. Yet she didn't hesitate before saying, "Of course." She told herself he was right—she needed to see his winery. But at the back of her mind was the desire to see more of him, as well. And that fact disconcerted her...briefly.

On the back of the piece of paper Grant Holcomb had written her address on, Bryce drew a map. "The winery is at the foot of a hill near some limestone caves. My house is here, on top of the hill." The line of road he drew, curved. "I call it Madrona, for the grove of madrona trees surrounding it."

"Sounds lovely. You mentioned earlier that you don't have tours. May I ask why?"

"I have private tasting only. My business is making wine, not conducting guided tours."

"It might provide good publicity," Sarah pointed out. "Your accountant could determine if it would be cost-effective."

Bryce frowned. "I don't care if it's cost-effective!"

A difficult client indeed, Sarah thought, irritated at the man's stubbornness. Working with him wasn't going to be easy.

Long after they had parted, Bryce Benedict was still on her mind as she sat at her desk. He was an unusual man, intense and reserved at the same time. *Very* attractive, though not precisely handsome.

And he didn't wear a wedding ring.

The thought flashed unbidden across her mind. She told herself immediately that of course it didn't matter. It didn't necessarily mean he was single. And besides, she wasn't interested in him as anything more than a lucrative client.

The direction of her thoughts so startled her that she got up and walked to stand at the window. Since she and John had become lovers, she'd never entertained even the briefest interest in another man. She wasn't sure that John could—or would—say the same. But she....

Enough of this, she told herself irritably. She went to her drawing board and began sketching ideas for wine labels. The label must be done immediately if Benedict Vintage Recherché was to be ready for launching in two months.

An hour later she gathered up her rough sketches and took them into the adjoining office.

"Working hard, Richard?" she asked.

Her graphic artist sat back in his chair, staring at the ceiling.

"Courting the muse," he replied with a dry chuckle, his black eyes dancing.

Sarah smiled in return. She'd rescued Richard Wong from the advertising jungle at Grant Holcomb's firm. A fine, well-trained graphic artist, his Chinese heritage showed in his sense of order, clear simple designs and low-key colors. Richard hadn't had the killer instinct necessary to survive in a large firm like Holcomb's, where political infighting was intrinsic to the job.

Richard never regretted leaving. Sarah always carefully attributed his work to him, instead of taking credit for it herself, as his previous boss had done.

"I'm trying to come up with something jazzy for Bay Radio," he explained.

"Give me a hand with these instead," Sarah said, passing him her sketches. "It's a rush job for Benedict Winery. Labels. The owner wants something simple but elegant, with the same logo. He made it clear the logo isn't to be changed by as much as a single stroke."

"That's what I like—a flexible client with an open mind," Richard answered dryly. "Hmm," he murmured as he considered the sketches. "Recherché... something new?"

Sarah explained about the new wine and its reasonable price.

"Good. It's about time wineries considered us peasants. I'd like to be able to afford something with a cork, for a change."

"Poor peasant," Sarah teased.

"So when do you want it?"

She hesitated.

Richard continued, "Oh no, don't tell me I have to cancel another date with Ginger?"

"I'll make it up to you. You can take her out to dinner tomorrow night on me."

"At the Blue Fox?" Richard asked hopefully, mentioning one of the most expensive restaurants in San Francisco.

"No, Scoma's."

"It's a deal."

"I'll pick up the sketches in the morning on my way to the Valley of the Moon, okay?"

"In the morning?" Richard grimaced, then finished good-naturedly, "All right. You know, it's true what they say about women bosses. You're slave drivers."

Sarah tossed him a brilliant smile as she left.

BRYCE SAT STARING AT A POSTER from the movie *Casablanca* in the bar of the restaurant of the same name. He'd spent a hectic afternoon running the errands he had saved for this visit to San Francisco. Now he relaxed over a glass of Perrier before the long drive home. The mellow atmosphere of the Casablanca, with its palm trees, candlelit mahogany tables and ceiling fans, was perfect for relaxing. But as Bryce looked up at the photo of Bogie and Bergman, he felt strangely unsettled.

He couldn't seem to put Sarah Montgomery out of his mind. She hadn't been at all what he expected. When Grant Holcomb recommended her, Bryce envisioned a mature battle-hardened type. A woman who could make it in the competitive world of advertising had to be tough, indeed. Instead, she was young, pretty, fresh. She was also clearly bright, talented and professional. But those qualities didn't detract one bit from her innate femininity.

What is it about her, he asked himself once more. He'd certainly met many women who were more beautiful. And despite her chic sophistication, he sensed that at heart she was as old-fashioned as her name. Sarah ... a plain name, yet softly appealing.

Was that it? That softness that made him wonder what it would be like to touch her, stroke her golden hair?

Bryce shook his head as if trying to shake her from his thoughts. It was ridiculous, he told himself, to speculate about her this way.

Taking a sip of Perrier, he looked once more at the photo of Humphrey Bogart and Ingrid Bergman. As he scrutinized it, he heard the pianist in a corner of the bar begin to play "As Time Goes By." Bryce's lips curved slightly in a half smile. Appropriate, he thought. And romantic.

Not like real life, he knew. In real life, true love sometimes ended not with a bang but a whimper. Instead of dramatic noble partings, there were interminable courtroom hassles and a piece of paper that said, "This marriage is dissolved."

Bryce's expression grew sober. Then, like metal drawn to magnet, his thoughts turned back to Sarah Montgomery. She probably liked *Casablanca*, probably cried at the end of it. He had a mental image of her brown eyes misted with tears. It was very appealing.

Enough, he told himself irritably.

Downing the last of the Perrier, he left the bar.

IT WAS A QUINTESSENTIAL San Francisco evening. The warmth of the day had turned cold with the setting sun. The lights of the city gleamed softly through the mist. A pale stream of fog swept in through the Golden Gate, blurring the string of lights across the Bay Bridge and blotting out the far shores of Berkeley and Oakland beyond. In her apartment, Sarah sat on the seat of the bay window reveling in the enchanting scene.

She'd been lucky to have found this place. Before leaving Minneapolis, when she was considering moving here, she'd read that the common denominator of housing in San Francisco was a view. Not only did she have that, she also had a wood-burning fireplace where now a log was burning brightly.

She lived on Telegraph Hill. Loma Alta—High Hill, the Spaniards called it. When she'd first moved to San Francisco she'd bought a guidebook and become a tourist to discover the different areas and neighborhoods. She used *Muni*, the public transportation system, to get to a particular destination and then she would walk—miles and miles.

Cable cars were also a favorite mode of travel. The camaraderie among the passengers, especially those standing on the steps outside the cable car as they made the roller-coaster ride up and down the hills, had added to the enchantment of her search for a

new home. It was carnivallike and uniquely San
Franciscan.

The day she had toured the Telegraph Hill district,
she treated herself to lunch at Enrico's Sidewalk
Café, then made the tour from Washington Square
in the heart of North Beach to the Coit Memorial
Tower. Standing on the observation deck at the top
of the tower, Sarah had gazed at the Golden Gate
Bridge spanning the entrance to the bay and linking
San Francisco with the Marin headlands. Not gold-
en, she had thought, but close—her artist's eye ap-
preciating the "international" orange of the bridge
and its cables threading through the graceful towers.
It was all bright and shining in the afternoon sun.

Suddenly her heart had felt too full as she let her
gaze travel back and forth across the vista before her.
She recognized Mount Tamalpais and Alcatraz, that
small rocky island in the middle of the bay. Though
she knew it was no longer a penitentiary, the very
sight of it caused a shiver to run down her spine. She
could see the ships and piers of the Embarcadero...
and the Ferry Building, where according to her
guidebook, the large hands on the tower clock
stopped and stayed stopped at 5:12 for exactly one
year after the earthquake on April 18, 1906. Directly
before her was the east slope of Telegraph Hill. She
turned and looked southwest to Russian Hill and
farther to catch just a glimpse of Grace Cathedral
atop Nob Hill. Nob Hill, she'd thought, the epicenter
of San Francisco's baronial wealth. And certainly
not too shabby an address.

Her own address was none too bad, either. Her
apartment was in a three-story building, picturesque, with brown-shingled walls and a grilled entrance gate that sheltered a laurel fig tree and pink
azaleas.

Turning from the window, Sarah looked around her living room. It was decorated in Laura Ashley prints in muted tones of sand and apricot. There were only a few pieces of furniture, but they were all cherished antiques. On a tall narrow Chippendale stand was an earthenware cream pitcher, given to her by Grandmother Ericson, filled with white daisies. On a low round table draped in a cloth of apricot checks were books of poetry and a silver framed photograph of her family taken last Christmas.

When the log in the fireplace crumbled into embers, she thought about the apartment in Minneapolis she'd shared with a girlfriend. There too the view overlooking one of the city's many beautiful parks was lovely. But they never had a fire burning in mid-August, and she knew now that she'd been waiting...for this. Not just this city, this place, but this life. The opportunity to be all that she could be. In a way, she mused, she was far from Minnesota and that apartment. But in another way, she wasn't.

I was right to come here, Sarah told herself. *I've got everything I ever wanted...a satisfying career, an exciting life in a glamorous city and a successful attractive man. Who could possibly want anything more? And still not thirty.*

Then, catching herself, she frowned slightly. The "big three-o," as Lara teasingly referred to it, was coming up soon. John had invited her to spend it in Paris with him, since he would be in Europe checking on the Stuttgart project. At the time it had seemed a marvelous idea. It was typical of John, who was generous and knew how to enjoy the good life he'd worked so hard to attain.

But now Sarah realized she'd probably be tied up with this Benedict account since her birthday would fall just before the wine was to premiere.

Thinking of John reminded her of Bebe's party.

All that happened to her today—the trip to Oakland,
coming back to find Bryce Benedict with his account
hers for the taking, making a dozen phone calls to
line up people and schedules—had erased the party
from her mind. It was ten o'clock now and the party
would just be getting into full swing. Well, she'd
write a note tomorrow explaining her absence.

She sighed, then finished the last of the wine in
her glass. She'd splurged and bought a bottle of
Benedict Chardonnay, a present to herself for landing such a big account.

It is excellent wine, she thought as she set down the
empty glass. And if she was going to appear bright
and competent when she talked to Bryce Benedict
tomorrow, she had better get to bed.

Rising, she turned out the lamp, then cast one
more glance out the window at the beautiful exciting city. In her mind's eye, she saw below one of her
favorite walks. Down Telegraph Hill all the way to
Sansome Street, which cut from Market to the Embarcadero. It was her place of exercise. Starting at the
top, near the Coit Tower, the red-brick Greenwich
Steps led down the east face of the hill. At the Montgomery and Filbert signpost, a staircase descended
to the Filbert Steps. Down that staircase was a verdant island. Really a street too steep to pave, it had
become a vertical garden of vines, roses and flowering trees, tended by the residents who lived along
either side. Further down were the concrete Filbert
Steps, which led to the waterfront. A walk or a jog
down then up those steps a couple of times a week
kept her in shape. At the first landing, a park bench
bore a plaque that read: "I have the feeling we're not
in Kansas anymore."

And neither am I, Sarah thought. *Not in Kansas or
Minnesota, but in a very different, very exciting place.
The absolutely perfect place for me.*

2

Sarah's red BMW nosed out of the mist on the Marin county side of the Golden Gate Bridge. The green slopes of Mount Tamalpais held back the fog, which drifted in wisps at its summit. Beyond picturesque Sausalito with its houseboat village, white sailboats dotted the brilliant blue of the bay.

As she sped past the architecturally acclaimed Marin Civic Center, the sunlight bright on its beautiful blue-tiled roof, she remembered it had been designed by Frank Lloyd Wright. At once her mind leapt to Bryce Benedict. His father had studied with Wright.

Bryce had said to take Highway 37 and then 121 to Sonoma. About an hour later she reached the old pueblo town. There was lots of Saturday traffic, but Sarah did not mind. She loved this place and so did John. They often drove up here to escape the city's summer fogs. She turned north onto Highway 12 and drove through the scenic countryside to the Valley of the Moon—Jack London country.

Long patterned rows of grapevines stretched over the valley floor and climbed the hills on each side. The vineyards looked rich and ripe now. Sun-drenched golden hills lay beyond.

Consulting the map Bryce had drawn for her, Sarah turned off the highway and followed a narrow country road. At the base of the hills a hand-carved redwood sign read Benedict Winery. Two massive stone buildings hugged the hillside. Beyond stood a long contemporary building. Functional, she supposed. And while a contrast to the old buildings, it integrated pleasantly into the setting. Driving slowly past, Sarah noted the date, 1880, chiseled above the arched doorway of one of the old vine-encrusted buildings.

So, Sarah thought, impressed. These were the original buildings Bryce's grandfather had built when he established the winery. It was all very lovely...the winery in a grove of eucalyptus trees, the vineyards rising on the hillsides. She felt a thrill of recognition from Bryce's description. Seeing this now, she could understand his strong sense of the value of what he was doing and his respect for tradition and family.

She experienced a sharp pang of envy, surprising herself. She'd been so eager to escape her own background, rejecting the role her mother embraced with such happiness and serenity.

For some inexplicable reason, Sarah thought of Kenny Olson. A Ph.D. at twenty-six, he taught English at the same prep school where her father was a teacher. Industrious, trustworthy, caring, he was everything a parent would want in a husband for their daughter. Her family still didn't know that Kenny was her real reason for leaving Minnesota. She had needed distance between herself and her large, close-knit, tradition-oriented family. She had wanted a very different life from the one her sister and mother had chosen. And she had it.

Workers moving around the buildings glanced curiously at the BMW as it passed, then ascended the road marked on her map.

Sarah drove slowly through a grove of eucalyptus, tall and slender, their distinctive aromatic perfume discernible even as she passed by. Then the silvery-gray-green of tree trunks changed from the eucalyptus to satiny cinnamon-red madrona trees gleaming against the shadows in the dense grove. Rounding a sharp curve, Sarah saw the house and brought the car to a stop.

Bryce Benedict's pride was indeed justified. A stunning house in a stunning setting. The home's dramatic horizontal planes and stone walls seemed to integrate into the hillside as if it too was one of the outcroppings that predominated this part of the country.

Two wings, paralleling at different levels, spanned a wooded ravine. The house was a magnificent combination of design and material—stone and wood and glass. Sarah knew enough to recognize an architectural masterpiece when she saw one. And *this* definitely was one.

Releasing the brake, she continued on up to the house where Bryce was just getting out of a sleek gray Jaguar.

He opened the door of her car and extended a big hand. For a brief moment their eyes held each other in silence.

My God, he's a disturbing man, Sarah thought. Picking up her purse and briefcase, she stepped out and took his hand.

Bryce smiled and the moment was broken. "Welcome to Madrona."

"It's absolutely sensational," Sarah said honestly. "I'm terribly impressed."

"I'm glad you like it. I'll show you the rest of it before we go through the winery, if you're interested."

"Of course I'm interested." She looked at the vine-covered hills and smiled at him. "The setting's not too bad either."

The huge oak door above the stone front steps burst open and a small boy ran toward Bryce. *So,*

Sarah thought, *there* is *a Mrs. Benedict*. She felt the sharp stab of an emotion she preferred not to identify.

"This is my son, Adam," Bryce said smiling down at the boy. His hand clasped the boy's shoulder. "Shake hands with Miss Montgomery, Adam."

Sarah held out a hand, but it took a gentle push from Bryce before Adam placed his small hand in hers. Glancing up at her through feathery dark lashes, he slowly gave her a shy smile. He looked a great deal like his father, with light brown hair and hazel eyes. Yet there was a tiny cleft in his chin that didn't come from Bryce.

When he looked away, Sarah wondered what on earth to say to such a child. Her own nieces and nephews never exhibited the slightest reticence in her presence, though she saw them only once or twice a year.

Finally, she asked, "Do you go to school, Adam?"

"This year I get to go to kindergar'n," he answered. Then he cast an appealing look at his father that clearly asked, *Can I go now?*

Bryce explained that he was going to show Miss Montgomery the house and winery. "Run along and play. We'll see you later."

Adam nodded. "I'll get Rex and Pancho," he said as he left.

"He's a handsome child," Sarah said as they entered the house. "Are Rex and Pancho man or beast?"

"Beasts," Bryce answered with a laugh. "Of course, you're absolutely right about Adam." The determinedly casual response couldn't mask his pride in the child.

From the outside, the entry appeared to be a continuation of the massive stone and redwood exterior wall. Inside, it was all glass and light. A polished slate floor bordered a skylit atrium that held masses of agapanthus. Sarah loved this particular variety of the lily-of-the-Nile. Some of the blossoms were white, but most were blue, their stems almost two feet tall. The lilies, like the rest of this place, were spectacular.

As they stepped into a living room with a wall of windows overlooking the madrona grove, a stocky middle-aged man rose from the sofa where he'd been reading the newspaper. He wore a close-trimmed full beard, sandy red like his thinning hair. His eyes were a bright blue and all that kept him from being quite handsome was his nose. Obviously it had been broken once and had not healed to duplicate its original shape. He was dressed too casually to be a butler, yet there was something about him—a deference—that indicated he was some kind of employee.

"Shall I make coffee, Bryce?"

"Please, Thaddeus. Sarah Montgomery, this is Thaddeus Harper. He's general factotum and basically keeps the place running."

"How do you do?" Sarah said politely.

Thaddeus smiled, clearly at ease in his role here. "Fine, thank you." Turning to Bryce, he said, "I'll serve it on the terrace." Then he offered to take Sarah's briefcase and indicated the guest bathroom off the hall. "You've had a long ride. Perhaps you'd like to freshen up before Bryce gives you the tour."

In the bathroom, Sarah noted the earth tones of the tile and wood. Russet-brown guest towels hung on the rack. One handsome piece of handcrafted pottery sat on the tiled vanity, a lidded jar done in soft beiges and blues. On one wall hung an excellent watercolor, a stormy seascape. As she powdered her nose and applied fresh lipstick, Sarah admired the richness of the color scheme, browns, beiges, rusts and blues. Handsome...neutral. Nothing at all delicate to indicate any woman's presence.

As Bryce quickly showed her around, Sarah noticed that indeed the entire house had a masculine air. There were none of the usual feminine touches, the furniture was stark and the magazines piled on the glass coffee table were all male oriented.

Still, it was *none* of her business, she reminded herself.

As they moved out onto the redwood terrace, Sarah said, "It's beautifully thought-out. I love the clean lines—the way spaces flow into one another. And the indoors and outdoors merging without rigid boundaries is most pleasing."

Bryce looked at her with interest. "You sound as if you know something about architecture."

"I...I have a friend who's an architect," she commented, wondering why she sounded so tense.

For a moment, Bryce watched her speculatively. Then he responded, "My father was a very talented man. And fortunate. My grandfather ran the winery until his death at eighty-six. So my father had a lot of time to practice his first love, architecture. The winery was just an avocation with him. For me, it's my life. But dad's vocation as an architect kept the family solvent."

Extremely solvent, Sarah thought, judging by the affluent way Bryce lived.

Deciding to risk a personal question, she asked, "Why didn't your father simply go off and be an architect?"

"He tried. The summer after finishing high school he rebelled and took off. Went to Wisconsin to meet his mentor. Later he was accepted into Wright's Taliesin Fellowship. Ironically, that summer he learned about Agoston Haraszthy...."

"Who left Wisconsin to bring grapevines here,"

Sarah finished for him. "How ironic, indeed." She smiled, and Bryce smiled with her.

He told her he was glad to see she knew something of wine history. Then he continued, "Well then, to make a long story short, dad felt fate had dealt him a lucky hand. He decided to come home and combine the best of both worlds."

"He was a lucky man."

"Yes." Bryce smiled again, with his eyes as well as his mouth.

The more Sarah learned about Bryce, the more interesting she found him. She sensed that something or someone had made him wary. But it obviously hadn't been his father, whom he clearly admired tremendously.

"Coffee time," Thaddeus called out as he approached, carrying a silver coffee service on a tray. He set it on a small redwood table, then left. Bryce poured for both himself and Sarah.

As she sipped the hot dark liquid, she asked, "Is this your first effort to be competitive? That is, to advertise?"

"Yes. We've always marketed our wine to a small clientele—restaurants, select liquor stores, private customers—via our own mailing list. Every year we release three wines, our Fumé Blanc, the Chardonnay—your favorite, I believe you said. And a Blanc de Blanc. Ours is a table wine, not a champagne wine. We sell out our inventory almost immediately."

Before he could continue, Sarah interrupted him to say she'd treated herself to a bottle of the Chardonnay to celebrate landing his account. She was rewarded with a warm smile.

"I want our new wine—Vintage Recherché— thanks to you, to do as well. Even though it won't be as exclusive."

"My designer, Richard Wong, said it was time

there was a corked wine affordable to the peasants," Sarah replied, sitting down at the table and reaching into the briefcase Thaddeus had placed there.

Bryce sat down also and took the sketches from her. To Sarah's immense relief, he smiled as he looked them over. "Good. *Very* good," he commented. Then, looking up at her, he said, "This is definitely what I had in mind. I'm glad Grant Holcomb recommended you." His hazel eyes darkened and seemed to change color as they changed expression. "You're a very pleasant surprise, Sarah Montgomery. Beautiful, as well as smart."

"Then, trust me..." Sarah began with a laugh and was startled to see a swift change cross the man's face. She wondered why the words she spoke challenged him. She'd meant to say something about if they could trust each other's creativity....

"Why don't we tour the winery now, if you've finished your coffee?" Bryce set down his cup. "I told Vince to expect us."

He led Sarah down a steep wooded path toward the winery. The stone buildings of Benedict Winery rose from a new tarmac courtyard and parking lot. Virginia creeper vines covered the exterior walls, outlining the arched doorways and windows. There were five or six cars in the parking lot and Sarah could see some men working in the back. Bryce commented that this would be the last quiet period for months. The men who were here today were longtime employees whose ranks would soon swell with the temporary help hired for the harvest.

"I want you to meet Vince. He's my chief enologist. We met at university. After graduation I returned to Madrona, but Vince went traveling. Worked in France, North Africa and South America. When I began looking for a wine maker to help put the sparkling wine into production, I thought I'd

track him down. He was working in New York State
in the champagne country."

"And you were able to lure him back to California. Was it difficult?" Sarah asked.

"A piece of cake. I lucked out. He'd met a young
lovely from around here and was trying to convince
her to settle back there. She was trying to convince
him to come here."

Sarah laughed. "Never underestimate the power
of a woman."

"Bingo!" Bryce said, laughing with her.

As she watched his appreciation of her jest lighten
his eyes, she thought again of how terribly aware
she was of this man—and not just as a client. In her
work she encountered many attractive men and certainly John was no ugly duckling. But there was
something indefinable about Bryce Benedict that
made her aware of him. And from somewhere deep
within, Sarah knew this sense of awareness was mutual. He found her attractive too, and that pleased
her.

As Sarah walked the last few feet across the tarmac and through the door he held open for her,
passing close enough to catch just a hint of the
essence of a soap or after shave lotion—a lime fragrance—she thought about chemistry. It is chemistry that converts the natural grape sugar into
alcohol. Chemistry that makes lovely wine from the
fruit of the vine. Sarah Montgomery, she told herself, you've been much too aware of this man ever
since you returned to your office and found him
waiting for you. Forget chemistry. Think money.
Pay attention so you can do a good job with this
campaign.

When they entered the main office, Sarah saw that
the walls were hung with the usual historic photographs of vineyards, equipment, houses and family
portraits.

"My grandfather and grandmother—Bryce and Isobel," her host explained, nodding at Sarah's quick glance. "Yes, I'm his namesake."

The next photograph was of his father and mother. Bryce bore a striking resemblance to his father, as little Adam did to him. Bryce's mother was a beautiful lady with a beautiful name. "Bianca—Italian for Barbara," he explained. "Her maiden name was Martella. She met my father in Florence on a Friday morning. By Sunday evening they knew they were in love. She married him the following Friday and came with him to Madrona. She never went home again."

He did not bother to explain the next photograph, which was a recent one of him and Adam. Adam's mother wasn't represented in this family gallery and Sarah was frankly curious since she didn't seem a presence in the house, either.

"I won't bore you with a lecture on the history of Benedict Winery," Bryce said, taking her arm and guiding her toward the long metal adjoining building. "I told you I'm the third generation of wine makers. We've each had different dreams and different problems. Prohibition almost destroyed my grandfather, but he hung on. My dad had to work his way through changes...and so have I."

They walked through the building that housed the thoroughly modern crushing and fermenting complex. Bryce pointed out the dump chutes where the grapes were fed into the crusher, then piped into the stainless-steel tanks. He remarked that most of the gear wineries use simply gather rust and dust from October until summer. "Then in July we clean everything—the gondolas, crushers, presses. The fermentation tanks must be cleaned and sterilized. All the machinery has to be thoroughly checked."

As they toured the facilities he explained that this would be the last free Saturday until harvest was completed. "Some of the grapes for the sparkling wine will be ready within the week. We pick those early—when the sugar content is low and the acid high."

"And the others?" Sarah asked.

"In theory," Bryce said with a wry smile, "wine grapes are ripe for picking fifty days after the first blush of color in their particular vineyard."

"But in practice...?" she encouraged.

"In practice, anywhere between forty-five and eighty days. Do you want me to tell you about our grapes? I don't know that you want to include this in your copy, but perhaps it will interest you."

Sarah assured him she'd find anything and everything useful. "We are a bit short on time, you know. Anything you can tell me will help."

He told her about their stock—Sauvignon Blanc, in the hierarchy of wine grapes outranked only by the Chardonnay and the White Riesling. Smiling at her, he said, "I don't want to insult your intelligence."

"Go ahead," Sarah said with a laugh, pleased with his obvious pride in his vineyard...pleased with the man himself, she admitted silently. Virile, handsome and owner of this beautiful place. *Nice combination,* registered a part of her mind while another part listened to his explanation of how the specific place a vine grows contributes characteristically to its fruit.

"Different lodes and pockets of earth yield different flavors and fragrances in the grape. We use Sauvignon Blanc grapes to make our Fumé Blanc— white smoke. Some say the taste of the grape is smoky. When they're ready for harvest, the grapes give off a misty blue dust." He turned as someone called his name. "Hello, Vince. Come and meet the lady who's going to handle the advertising."

Sarah turned to see a lean tan-faced man walking

toward them. "Hello," she said, holding out her hand.

"Sarah Montgomery—Vince Ventura," Bryce said. "I was just telling her about our white smoke. You want to add anything more?"

"Hi, Sarah." He shook hands with her, then said, "Bryce really connected with something I told him about harvest time when I was in France in the Loire Valley. The dust from those grapes literally hung in a mist in the cool autumn air. It was a beautiful sight to see."

Smiling at him, Sarah said, "That's quite poetic. Perhaps we can find a spot for that in our copy. Do you want to be quoted?"

"Not especially," Vince replied, grinning. "Quote Bryce on everything. Especially if there are going to be any mistakes." Excusing himself, he said he was running sugar tests in the vineyard. "I think we should start picking Luis's Pinot Noirs." As he turned away, he grinned at Sarah and said, "Write something wonderful."

Looking after Vince, she mused, "Complicated, isn't it?" Then she smiled up at Bryce and asked, "Do you have a simple textbook? Perhaps one entitled *Grapes—From the Vine to the Glass in Five Easy Steps*. I told you I've been on several winery tours. I must have only tasted, not listened. I'm afraid to ask too many questions. Afraid to reveal how much I don't know. You might decide you'd been hasty... hiring me."

Those hazel eyes considered her steadily. Then, very softly, Bryce said, "I don't think so." He spoke deliberately, slowly, all the while holding her gaze with his.

He'd exhibited the same charming boldness yesterday just before they went to lunch. He's a very self-confident man, she told herself and hoped her expression did not reveal that today her pulse quickened even more in response to his directness than it had twenty-four hours earlier.

"The grapes Vince referred to are the ones for the new wine. He'll have them picked at twenty degrees Brix—that's a reading for sugar—to minimize color and to retain acidity. The wine will be fruity, but absolutely dry and tart."

"In other words—wonderful." Without thinking, Sarah tucked her hand in the crook of his arm and said, "Show me where you age that marvelous Chardonnay."

As they walked into the cooling caves, Bryce said, "We use French oak cooperage for our Chardonnay. That's how my grandfather got his start. He was a cooper—made the barrels. Saved his money, bought a small piece of this vineyard first. Later he acquired more land. My dad added more acreage for Pinot Noir grapes for this new line."

"And you?" Sarah asked. "Will you add more land too?"

"No. At the moment I want to concentrate on adding wine to a market." His manner was easy. He obviously enjoyed talking about his wines. "Our tanks are temperature controlled, so we can ferment the wine a bit more slowly. That preserves the bouquet. Then the touch of oak on the white wine—" he paused and grinned at Sarah, then continued "—makes our Chardonnay rich, complex and elegant. That's why you appreciate Benedict Chardonnay. Shows you have excellent taste."

"Of course," she teased, "Grant Holcomb told you I did. That's why you hired me, remember?"

He looked directly at her and Sarah was very much aware that the two of them were enjoying this tour. She forced herself to think of what she might

need to know for copy. "How long is your...my...
Chardonnay aged?"

In a thoughtful tone, Bryce told her that aging
varies. "Part of what makes wine making exciting is
the fact that *change* is the only constant." He looked
down at Sarah. "Does that sound like double-talk?"

She withdrew her hand from his arm and walked
a few steps away from him. "No. I think what you
are saying is every wine maker decides his own
changes—his own interpretation of when the grape
has become the wine."

Looking around at the vast amount of cooperage—gallons and gallons of wine aging in the careful process— she thought about the other equipment
she'd seen; the glass-enclosed laboratory, the fully
automatic bottling equipment. The winery was not
operated on the proverbial shoestring. This attractive intense man said he wanted to concentrate on
adding a wine to the market. He obviously had the
means to do so.

Bryce Benedict had stormed into her office yesterday, angry with Grant Holcomb. Furious, although
his behavior had not been violent. Now the two of
them stood here in the heart of his place of business,
well on their way to achieving something wonderful
and important.

Something about all this pleased her very much.
Thank you, Grant Holcomb, she thought, and an ironic
smile curved her lips.

"My head is spinning," she said, turning to look
at Bryce.

He laughed. "You must be hungry. Let's go have
lunch."

As they walked toward the door, Sarah stopped in
front of a huge oak cask. Painted on its face in Old-
English lettering was an inscription:

Back of this Wine is the Vintner,
And back through the years, his Skill;
And back of it all are the Vines in the Sun
And the Rain
And the Master's Will.

"How beautiful," Sarah murmured, lightly trac-
ing the words. "It's true, isn't it?"

Bryce nodded. "Yes, it's true. You must have
patience... and the gambling instinct. You live on a
tightrope because many of the factors that affect
your grapes aren't in your control. 'The sun and the
rain and the Master's will.'"

Sarah looked up at him, drawn by his intensity. He
was close to the earth in a way she could appreciate.
She'd spent many of her summer vacations with her
mother's people. Grandfather Ericson farmed wheat
in the Red River Valley. With a start, she realized
that Bryce was speaking again of the harvest.

"It's a long battle from March when the first
swelling of the leaf buds appear, until October when
the grapes are in the crusher. We pray for rain and
sun and no frost. And that the deer won't maraud
the vines and the birds won't eat too many of the
grapes."

As they came out of the cooling cave, blinking in
the brilliant sunlight, he finished, "Otherwise, it's a
piece of cake."

Sarah laughed with him. "Nicely put. Shall I use
that in the copy? Seriously, I'm fascinated. The old
and the new... oak casks and stainless-steel tanks.
Tradition... and progress."

As they followed the steep path leading back to
the house, Sarah's mind returned to the question
that had been nagging at her since her arrival.
Bryce's wife. Was he married, divorced or widowed?

"I hope you have some idea of what you'll need now," he said, interrupting her reverie.

"Photos first, for the brochure."

"Blast! I left my photos at Holcomb's office when I walked out after firing him." He shot her a wry look.

"I'm sure we can pick them up on Monday."

They walked along, surrounded by the late-summer air, the pungent fragrance of the eucalyptus and madrona trees all around them.

"I've been giving you my twenty-five-cent-tour lecture," Bryce said with a smile. "I hope I haven't bored you out of your mind."

"I'd pay at least double that amount," she said, returning his smile.

Bryce turned to look directly into her eyes. "You're the perfect audience." Then he added, "And a beautiful one." The last was spoken so softly she scarcely heard the words. Looking up at the dancing lights in his hazel eyes, Sarah found herself tempted to raise on her tiptoes and lay her lips against the half smile curving his mouth. The moment was as highly charged as a bottle of champagne. Then Adam appeared, running down the path to join them.

"Thaddeus says lunch is ready."

The round table was set in the shade on the terrace, a crisp white-linen cloth complimented by rust napkins, elaborately folded. Bryce told Thaddeus to start serving. "I'll be right back," he said, looking mysterious.

As Thaddeus served chicken breasts sautéed in white wine, fettuccini with pesto sauce and a salad of crisp bibb lettuce, Bryce returned carrying an opened bottle of unlabeled wine and four slender wine goblets. "This is it," he announced, pouring a small amount into her glass. He held it to the light before he offered it to her.

It was a lovely rosy red, bright and sparkling as

the sunlight mixed with the effervescence Sarah watched bubbling up from the bottom of the glass. "Lovely color," she said. Then, taking the goblet, she held it to her nose and sniffed the bouquet. Again she nodded, and looking at Bryce repeated, "Lovely...very nice. There's something I can *almost* identify that's intriguing."

"That's good." Bryce winked at Thaddeus. "Intrigue invites the customer to buy again."

Sarah took a sip of the wine, rolling it around in her mouth. It tasted heavenly, lively and delicate. "What is that flavor...there's something different. It's fruity? No, there's just the barest hint of something spicey...no, that's not what I mean." She smiled broadly at them all and sipped the wine again. After she had thoroughly enjoyed the taste of the wine on her tongue, she swallowed and sighed. "I love it," she said.

Bryce, who had been watching her, laughed aloud. Thaddeus and Adam joined him in the laughter. "Wonderful!" He filled her glass, then Thaddeus's and his. He pretended to pour a drop for Adam, winking at the boy as he did so. "I'm not sure what we'd have done if you'd hated it." When he had seated himself between her and Adam, he added, "I'll send a case home with you. You can drink it for inspiration when you're writing the copy."

As they were savoring the delicious lunch, Bryce asked, "Do you ever miss the snows of Minnesota now that you live here in 'lotus land'?"

"Actually, I couldn't wait to get out of there," Sarah replied with a chuckle. "I wanted to do something different with my life...something exciting and challenging."

"And you've succeeded?" Bryce's eyes darkened as he waited for her answer. "You've put all that small-town life behind you?"

Defensively she replied, "Faribault isn't San Francisco, of course, but neither is it the boonies. Minnesota isn't exactly darkest Africa."

A telephone shrilled inside the house and Bryce rose, declining Thaddeus's offer to answer it. "That's undoubtedly for me. We're expecting some new equipment today."

In a moment he was back, apologizing. "I'm needed at the winery...seems there's been an error in the shipment. Enjoy your dessert. I'll be back shortly."

Thaddeus cleared the table and served a fluffy chocolate mousse. He chatted easily with Sarah about the weather and living in the wine country.

Adam said nothing until he finished his dessert and laid down his spoon. Looking directly at Sarah, he said, "My mother lives in Africa."

Sarah gave an inward sigh, hoping he wasn't one of those children who tell tall tales for attention. "Really?" she replied in an attempt to keep the conversation going.

"She's uh...uh...archaeologis'." His childish tongue stumbled over the long word.

"That's very interesting, Adam," Sarah said, encouraging him.

"Finished, Adam?" Thaddeus interrupted, gathering up the dishes. "Time for a short rest," he said in an affectionate yet no-nonsense tone.

"I'm not tired."

Thaddeus shook his head. "Off with you now. Miss Montgomery's here to do some work. She'll be here when you've finished resting."

"More coffee?" Thaddeus asked when Adam had gone reluctantly.

Sarah nodded. As he poured it, she said, "He seems a rather lonely little boy."

"Yes," Thaddeus admitted with a small sigh.

"We're quite isolated up here. I hope things will be better when he starts school next month. On a regular basis, that is. He's been attending nursery school a couple of days a week. I take him and do errands in town while I wait. He'll like kindergarten. Of course then Bryce will be even lonelier. He spends lots of time with Adam."

Sarah cocked her head to one side and eyed Thaddeus speculatively. "Do you mind if I ask how you met Bryce?"

Thaddeus smiled. "I'm not most people's idea of a housekeeper, I know." He leaned back in his chair and relaxed. "I was a friend of Luis, Bryce's father. We grew up together. I guess one reason we were so close is that we both had a strong sense of wanderlust. We each wanted to get out of this valley, see the world, do exciting different things. While Luis became an architect, I led a more eclectic life — amateur boxing, serving on the crew of a tramp steamer, teaching English in the Middle East and Africa."

Sarah said with a touch of awe in her voice, "It certainly sounds as if your life hasn't been dull."

"No — never that." He sighed. "But it got old after a while. When you're twenty the sailor's dream of a girl in every port sounds wonderful. By the time you're thirty-five, it's like being on a treadmill — you're going nowhere fast. I came back here to visit Luis, and about that time Bryce became very ill. He had to remain at home for six months. Luis asked me to stay on as a live-in tutor. Before Bryce was fully recovered, Bianca died. Luis was having a bad time. I stayed on to help manage things and just never left."

He gave Sarah a frank, guileless look. "It's a life that suits me perfectly. I enjoy living here, I have a family, something I've not had for a very long time. This is an efficient house to manage. Best of all, I

have plenty of free time to devote to my poetry."
He grinned, half-embarrassed and half-proud. "I'm
by way of being something of a minor celebrity in
these parts. But it's not something I can make a living at."

Sarah grinned ruefully, understanding what he
was saying. She knew lots of copywriters who were
also struggling poets or novelists.

Unable to contain her curiosity any longer, Sarah
asked, "Is Adam's mother in Africa? Or does the
child have a strong imagination?"

Thaddeus's kind expression hardened quickly.
"Adam was telling the truth. She's an archaeologist
working in Africa. A couple of years now." Thaddeus shook his head. "Divorced. She shouldn't have
married, had the child, if she couldn't make a lifetime commitment."

Then, as if aware he'd gone too far, he straight-
ened and rose. "If you'd like to work, Miss Montgomery, you could use the study."

It was only when Bryce entered the study that
Sarah realized how much time had gone by. She had
been so engrossed in putting down copy from her
tour of the winery and the tasting of the Recherché,
the afternoon passed without her realizing it.

"Sorry I was so long," he apologized, explaining
that a component was missing from the piece of
machinery just delivered. "We need that equipment
for next week." He went on to say he'd been all this
time on the phone.

"I've managed to accomplish quite a lot," Sarah
said, showing him the sheets of typewritten copy.
"This is a lovely place to work." She turned to look
out at the vineyards color-coding the hillsides, then
back to Bryce. Indicating the framed photographs on
the wall, vineyard country and two of the ocean—all
beautifully composed, their sensitivity reaching out

to the viewer—she added, "Did you take those marvelous photographs?"

He looked pleased. "A hobby of mine," he said.

"More than a hobby, I think. Those are professional!"

"Thanks for the kind words. I hope you like the ones I left with Holcomb."

"I can't wait to see them." She began stuffing her papers into her briefcase.

"Sarah, there's an August Moon concert at Charles Krug Winery tonight. Since I've taken up your whole Saturday with work let me make it up to you. Please attend the concert with me and stay overnight."

Surprised, she looked at him.

Before she could answer, he added, "Unless, of course, you have other plans for this evening."

"No, I don't have any plans, but," she paused, then continued, "I didn't plan to stay, nor am I dressed for a concert." She'd dressed casually in white linen slacks and a peach-colored silk blouse.

"It's very informal," he said. "You're fine." He told her Thaddeus was always prepared for guests. "He keeps an extra supply of toothbrushes and he'll find a robe and pajamas for you. And absolutely overwhelm you with a special dinner."

For a moment, Sarah considered. A part of her wanted to leave at once... *because* she wanted to stay. But another part was drawn to this man, wanting to know him better.

Just then Adam came running into the room. "Hi," he said, smiling up at his father. Then including her in his greeting, he shyly repeated, "Hi."

Impulsively she replied, "It sounds like fun."

THE GRAY JAGUAR purred smoothly down the Madrona hill between rows of vineyard shadowed by the full moon gleaming in the clear night sky. Charles Krug Winery was surrounded by a grove of tall oak trees. Bryce took her arm as they walked toward the huge lawn where tables were set up for the audience. The string quartet was preparing to perform on the front steps of the stone winery building.

Bryce ordered wine immediately, since serving was discontinued as soon as the concert began. He lifted his glass to Sarah. Their fingers touched as the glasses clinked. Sarah felt a strange tingle run down her arm and through her body. This Bryce Benedict affected her in a way no other man had ever done... and yet, he was the kind of man she had never wanted to be involved with.

"My father used to play violin in this group," Bryce commented.

"Do you play?"

"A little. Not as well as he did. What about you?"

"Oh, everyone in my family plays some instrument. We used to have our own little recitals."

She smiled, remembering the familiar scene. John didn't care for chamber music, he preferred jazz. It had been a while since she'd been to a concert like this.

A hush fell over the audience as the first strains of Mozart's Quintet in G Minor rose in the air. From the first note the mellow resonance of the strings drew the music as clearly on the air as an artist draws upon the canvas. Sarah listened breathless and enthralled. Bryce too seemed lost in passionate concentration as the adagio movement began. The harmony of the strings sang full and vibrant. The viola answered, in echoes, the violins. It was all so beautiful... the music, the full August moon spreading its lambent glow over the towering trees and old buildings. Bryce's hand covered hers, and she turned her palm up to clasp his big hard hand. They seemed

joined at that moment in the soaring sounds of the
music, totally one in emotional response to the power
of Mozart's genius.

The music progressed through the minuetto and
began the first adagio movement. Again Sarah heard
the singing refrain of the violins and the viola,
answering.

Suddenly she thought of an evening when she
and John had been driving home in his car. When a
Mozart program had been announced, John reached
to change the station. Sarah had pleaded with him,
telling him how much she loved Mozart. He had
smiled and said okay, whatever the lovely lady
wanted.

As she'd listened to the music, she'd asked John
what he thought the violins and viola were saying to
each other. He had responded teasingly, "I don't
speak violin."

Somehow she couldn't tell him, "They're saying 'I
love you.' And the viola answers, 'I love you.'"
Those were words John couldn't—or wouldn't—
say. He told her he adored her, but it wasn't nearly
the same thing.

Now, as Bryce's hand covered hers, she dared not
look at him. She was afraid to reveal how completely
she was transported outside herself.

Sitting there beside him, she *knew* that this was a
man who could say "I love you."

When the last notes died away, there was a long
moment of silence as though the audience was
stunned by the beauty of what they had just experienced. Then they broke into applause.

The ride home was nearly silent. It had been such
a beautiful evening, Sarah was reluctant to speak.
Words might shatter this fragile enchantment. The
very night was filled still with singing violins and
heady wine. And this man. Something incredible

had happened to her there in the moonlight, an emotional joining she'd never felt before.

Deep shadows lay around Madrona as the huge orange moon slipped toward the western horizon. As she stepped out of the Jaguar, Sarah looked up directly into Bryce's face. Then, still without speaking, he held out his hand and she placed hers in his. Together they walked up the steps toward the house. Pausing before the door, he turned and looked down at her. His gaze traveled slowly over her face, rested on her mouth and she knew she wanted to feel his warm lips hard against hers as she'd never wanted anything before. Sarah waited. This man was taking her measure and she was permitting him to do so.

His gaze returned to her eyes and she saw the brown marbling the yellow until his eyes darkened like a banked fire. She read desire in them and knew he read the same in hers. Fascinated, she watched the lids, fringed in heavy lashes, slowly descend as he drew her into his arms. She leaned into his embrace, her arms reaching around his broad shoulders, all her being yearning toward him. When his mouth took hers it was as though the whole world was obliterated...there was nothing except the two of them, enfolded in moonlight.

3

SARAH STOOD ON the wide stone steps of Madrona, waiting for Thaddeus to bring her car around. The morning sun cast long shadows of the madrona trees across the driveway. Thaddeus had urged her to delay her departure until Bryce returned from the hillside vineyard where he went to test for sugar. But Sarah insisted that she had to get back to the city.

She couldn't face Bryce so soon after that kiss in the moonlight. She needed time to recover, to think, to put distance between them.

Why on earth did I do it, she asked herself for the hundredth time. She was in love with someone else. And even if she wasn't, Bryce wasn't the kind of man who would fit into her life.

Just then Thaddeus pulled up in front of Sarah. He held open the door while she got into the car.

"Are you sure you can't wait? Bryce will want to say goodbye, I'm sure."

"I'm sorry. My briefcase is full of work," Sarah said, only half lying. Her briefcase *was* full of work, but that wasn't what prompted her hurried departure.

"Very well. It was nice meeting you, Sarah. I'm sure we'll be seeing you here again."

He closed the door firmly, then stepped back.

As Sarah drove off, she noticed that Adam had come out to sit on the top step. She rolled down the window and leaned out to wave goodbye to him. He didn't wave back.

As she guided her car down the steep driveway, she knew Adam was angry at her sudden leave-taking. She felt an awful stab of guilt, but told herself defensively that she couldn't do anything about it.

Driving through the brilliant morning sunshine toward the city, Sarah tried to plan her day ahead. She decided to call Richard and see if he was free to work. But she couldn't concentrate on her plans. Her usually efficient mind seemed to be muddled today, unable to concentrate, full of last night's moonlight and music. Never before had she experienced the intense rapport she had shared with Bryce at the concert.

"Blast!" she said out loud, hitting the steering wheel with the palm of her hand. *Why did this have to happen? I wasn't looking for it. It just complicates my perfectly nice little life. Everything is just the way I want it now. I don't need Bryce throwing a monkey wrench into things.*

She had been away from John too long, she told herself. Last night she had just been feeling lonely and vulnerable. When she saw John tomorrow everything would be fine again. And Bryce would be nothing more than a client.

Parking her car in the Union Square garage, she took a bottle of the wine Bryce had given her and walked across Stockton Street to her office.

The building was quiet today since most of the offices were closed. Sarah called Richard, who grumbled good-naturedly about working on his day off. A half hour later, he was there.

When Sarah handed him the wine, he said, "Hey, you don't have to bribe me."

She smiled. "Yes, I do." Opening her briefcase, she

took out some papers. "As I told you the other day, Bryce wants to use the same Benedict Winery logo, the *B* and *W* intertwined in a medieval-style illumination."

As Richard glanced at the logo, he said, "That's fine. It's rather old-fashioned, but definitely classy."

"And this is the label we'll use," Sarah continued, showing Richard the sketch with Bryce's corrections.

"Interesting. The man actually improved slightly on our work."

"To work, slave," Sarah teased. "These labels have to be done immediately, if not sooner, so the wine bottles and cartons can be labeled. The wine's going to be released right after harvest in October."

"Whew! That *is* fast work. But don't worry. I'll get it done."

"I know you will. Richard, in case I don't say it often enough, I deeply appreciate how hard you work. You contribute a great deal to the success of this firm. Without you, we wouldn't be where we are today."

Embarrassed, Richard mumbled, "Hey, it's okay."

Sarah was touched by his modesty. But she had no intention of letting her sincere compliment end with Richard's shy acceptance. She continued, "When this rush job is over and we have a chance to breathe again, I'd like to talk to you about a promotion." She finished with a sly grin, "If you're interested."

He smiled broadly. "*If* I'm interested! Yes, I'm interested! Wait till I tell Ginger. She's always saying I need to be more ambitious."

"How are things with you two?" Sarah asked. She knew Richard well enough to be aware that he and his girlfriend had had some rocky times.

"Better," he answered frankly. "She's beginning

to accept that it means more to me to enjoy what I'm doing than to earn a fortune. And I'm beginning to accept that a woman has a right to some semblance of security before she settles down with a guy."

"In other words, you're both compromising," Sarah commented.

"Yeah, I guess so." He raised one dark eyebrow quizzically. "Interesting concept, compromise."

Sarah laughed. "You sound like you just invented it."

Richard grinned disarmingly. "Well, I may not have invented it, but I sure just discovered it. I suspect I could have avoided a lot of arguments, slammed doors and name-calling if I'd discovered it sooner." He finished dryly, "Of course, I would have missed all the making up afterward too. So maybe it's good I'm just now beginning to get wise."

"You're incorrigible."

"That's what Ginger says. Well, I'd better get to work before I get fired instead of promoted."

He took the sketch and bottle of wine into his office. For the rest of the day, Sarah worked on the copy for the brochure and ad campaign. The phone rang several times, but she didn't answer it. She told herself she didn't want to interrupt her work, but the truth was she was afraid it might be Bryce. And she had no idea what to say to him.

That kiss had thrown her for a loop. In all the time she'd been involved with John, she'd never felt more than the mildest twinge of attraction for another man. And she'd certainly never acted on any attraction she did feel. Whatever John's feelings might be on the subject of fidelity, the fact was that Sarah was definitely a one-man woman. She'd never been the type to line up one date after another with a succession of men, even in college.

From the moment she'd first met John, she'd felt he was all she could possibly want. Making love with him constituted a commitment, as far as she was concerned. They might not be married or engaged or even living together, but they were definitely involved. And as far as she was concerned, that involvement precluded affairs with other men.

It was hardly an affair, it was just a kiss, she reminded herself forcefully.

But her heart replied, "Oh, what a kiss!"

THE NEXT MORNING, Lara buzzed Sarah to tell her that John was on the phone.

Sarah hesitated before finally picking up the receiver.

"Hi," she said, trying to sound like her bright cheery self.

She wasn't sure if it was her imagination or if there really was a note of guilt in her voice.

"I tried all weekend to reach you," John replied. "Did you run away from home?"

His tone was teasing and Sarah reaized she was being foolish in thinking she sounded anything other than her usual self.

"No, I didn't run away. I just worked like crazy. I was busy with a new client." Somehow, she didn't want to share details of her trip to Madrona with John, so she didn't explain further.

"Well, I'm back in town finally."

"Good. I've missed you."

"I've missed you too. I'll tell you just how much, tonight. How about dinner?"

"How about lunch?" she countered.

"I wish I could. But I'm so busy taking care of business that piled up on my desk while I was gone, that I can't do it."

Sarah sighed with disappointment. "The hazards

of being incredibly successful. Well, why don't I
meet you at your place after work?"

"Okay. You know, we've got to discuss Hawaii. I
have to leave even sooner than I expected—Wednesday."

"Wednesday?" Sarah's voice rose in dismay. "That
doesn't give us much time."

"I can't help it. A problem came up over there. But
it doesn't really matter since you'll be coming shortly anyway."

Avoiding his last comment, Sarah asked, "How
long will you have to be there?"

"A month, at least. Maybe longer. Sorry, love. I
know you must be starting to think of me as the invisible boyfriend."

"It's all right. Honestly. I understand."

"Well, it sounds like you're getting pretty busy
yourself." He finished, "I've got to run. Robb's
calling. See you tonight, Sarah."

She hung up, but for a long moment she didn't
move. For the first time in two years, she felt am-
bivalent about seeing John. It wasn't guilt. After all,
she told herself again, one kiss, while beguiling,
didn't constitute infidelity. And besides, John had
never asked for fidelity, or offered it.

What am I afraid of, she asked herself. *That I'll see
John and not feel the same about him? That's silly. He'll
be as handsome and charming as ever and I'll be overcome, as always, by that old magic. I just need to be with
him, that's all. It's been too long. Bryce touched loneliness
in me. Nothing more.*

Determinedly, she went back to work. But any
idea she had of putting Bryce out of her mind was
destroyed when he called a few minutes later.

Even over the telephone, his voice was like an
electric charge. To her relief, he said nothing about
the weekend, but came straight to the point.

"I'm coming into the city tomorrow to pick up those photos from Holcomb. How about if I drop them off in the afternoon?"

"Fine. I should be here all day tomorrow." Anxious to cut the conversation short, she finished, "I'll see you then. Goodbye."

She knew she'd been a bit too abrupt, but she couldn't help it. An extended conversation with Bryce, especially any mention of that kiss, was exactly what she wanted to avoid right now. Just the thought of seeing him tomorrow was disturbing enough.

But she found it hard to concentrate on work. Finally, in the middle of the afternoon, she told Lara she was leaving early to do some shopping.

A few minutes later, she walked into Neiman-Marcus's gleaming new ultramodern building on the corner of Union Square. She stopped at the candy counter to buy a pound of Godiva chocolates, John's favorites. Then she took the escalator up to the third floor. For an hour she browsed through the lingerie department, trying on then discarding various items.

Finally she chose a deliciously sensuous negligee in a luscious ripe berry color. The gown was made entirely of sheer lace and had a low-cut, fitted bodice.

The perfect thing to welcome John home in, Sarah thought. Tonight would be a romantic fantasy, like other nights they had had together. And Bryce would be the furthest thing from her mind.

At seven o'clock sharp that night, Sarah rang the bell at John's Russian Hill apartment. It was on the ninth floor of a new building that was starkly modern, all glass and steel. John's apartment was decorated in the same contemporary manner—chrome-and-glass tables and off-white furniture.

The few paintings on the stark white walls were Leroy Neiman sports prints.

When Kwan, John's Taiwanese houseboy, let Sarah in, she heard John call to her through the half-open door to his bedroom.

"Sorry I'm running late, love. It was hectic today! I appreciate you coming over here. It saves time."

She walked into the bedroom and found John standing in front of a mirror, struggling with his tie. Turning to face her, he flashed a brilliant smile.

He was handome, Sarah thought. Tall and elegantly slim. If he ever wanted another career, he could be a model.

His dark good looks always brought glances of admiration from other women. In Lara's words, he was a perfect ten. The obvious envy of other women made Sarah feel proud and lucky that he was hers. Well—*most* of the time he was hers, she thought dryly.

"Come here," he commanded softly.

She walked up to him, stopping only inches from him.

He reached out and gently traced the line of her cheek. "You are lovely. And I missed you."

His voice was husky, deep with meaning. Sarah felt her heart reach out to him.

Everything is fine she told herself, immensely relieved. *I was right.* Just seeing him again was all she needed.

Leaning toward her, he kissed her tenderly with a hint of the passion that would come later. It was sweet, and Sarah enjoyed it. And yet...to her utter chagrin, John's kiss had none of the potent force of Bryce's. It awakened pleasant memories in her, but it didn't stir her soul.

Pulling away, Sarah walked over to the floor-to-ceiling window, which offered a magnificent view.

Before her lay the Golden Gate Bridge ablaze with lights, the hills of Marin County, Richmond Bridge and the Bay Bridge. It was a breathtaking sight. John never settled for less than the best, even in a view.

From behind her, he said, "I made reservations at Maxwell's Plum for eight. We'd better hurry."

He took her hand, smiled down at her happily, and they left the apartment.

Maxwell's Plum was an ornately decorated restaurant in the famed Ghirardelli Square. The lushly baroque atmosphere combined art deco and art nouveau. John and Sarah sat at a table next to the window overlooking the bay. As they ate wild boar and duckling Normande, John told Sarah about his trip. He was an interesting conversationalist, witty and amusing.

Sarah thoroughly enjoyed the food, the happily decadent atmosphere and talking with John. As they lingered over dessert, he suddenly pulled a small package from his pocket.

"Just a little something to let you know I was thinking of you during the trip," he said, smiling modestly.

When Sarah unwrapped the package, she found the most magnificent watch she'd ever seen—the thinnest platinum band, tiny rubies encircling the face.

She was speechless for a moment. John often gave her generous gifts, but this, she knew, must have cost a small fortune.

Watching her, he teased, "Don't tell me you'd prefer a Timex?"

She laughed softly and shook her head. "No," she answered, her voice tremulous.

He reached out and put it on her narrow wrist. Then he slowly brought her hand to his lips and kissed it softly. For a moment, his eyes held hers.

There was a genuine warmth in his expression that touched Sarah deeply. She sensed that he enjoyed giving this gift every bit as much as she enjoyed receiving it.

"Now, then," he continued, "about Hawaii—"

"John," Sarah interrupted quickly, "I can't go."

"What!"

"I told you I have a new account—Benedict Winery. It's the biggest thing I've ever tackled, and a rush job at that. There's simply no way I can take off two weeks or even two days right now."

For one split second she thought he was going to react angrily. She half expected him to say, "Forget your work, damn it, come with me."

Suddenly she realized she wanted him to say that, needed to hear him say that it had been too long and that he needed her.

But the moment passed. Finally he sighed and said, "I see. Well, I'm disappointed of course. But I can understand how much this means to your business."

He *understood*. Naturally, Sarah thought, intensely disappointed. Their relationship was based on understanding, on not asking for sacrifices of each other. He was the quintessential new liberated male, not trying to hold down a woman in any way.

I should be glad, Sarah thought, *that he respects the importance of my work as much as his own*. But she wasn't! All of this "understanding" meant that they wouldn't see each other for a month, maybe two. And she very much doubted that he would spend all of that time thinking of her.

After a tense silence, John asked, "What's wrong? It won't be forever, you know. And we still have tonight and tomorrow night...." His voice trailed off suggestively.

But suddenly all thoughts of her sexy new negli-

gee went out of Sarah's mind. All she knew was that
she wanted to be alone. She was hurt and angry, and
yet perversely she realized she had no right to feel
this way.

"I'm just exhausted," she lied. "It was...a hard
weekend, working on this new account."

After a moment, she added, not meeting John's
look, "If you don't mind, I'd like to make this an
early evening. Will you take a rain check for tomorrow night?"

John's expression hardened slightly. He was clearly irritated. "Okay," he finally said in a tight voice.

Motioning to the waiter, he asked for the bill.
When it came, he paid promptly, then led Sarah out
of the restaurant.

At her apartment, he kissed her once, briefly, then
told her he would call tomorrow. A moment later,
he was gone.

Inside, Sarah leaned against the door for a moment. *I'm a fool*, she told herself. *I could have had tonight and tomorrow night.*

But that wasn't enough.

TUESDAY BEGAN WITH A PHONE CALL before Sarah's alarm
went off.

"Hello," she answered sleepily.

"Good morning." It was John. "I think we got
our signals mixed last night," he said. "I must have
been still suffering from jet lag." He went on to say
that finding her more engrossed with work than
being with him had disconcerted him, he supposed.
Would she accept that as an explanation or apology
or whatever it took to put the "love light" back into
her beautiful brown eyes?

"I'm sorry too," she told him, *wanting* to feel that
familiar emanation of magic that usually came from
just hearing the warmth of his tone. "What's your
schedule like today?" she asked, thinking that they
could make plans now for lunch as well as for the
evening.

"Frantic. All day. There are several last-minute
decisions Robb and I have to make. But," he finished, "tonight's reserved just for us. Dinner may be
late, but it'll be very nice." His voice dropped to an
intimate whisper, "I missed you, my lady. I especially missed you last night."

All the time Sarah was getting dressed, she thought
about her lack of response to John's voice ... words ...
suggestiveness.

Obviously, he didn't sense any lack. Perhaps, she
thought, he wasn't as preoccupied with her as she

was with him. No perhaps about it. She knew he wasn't. And until now, that hadn't mattered.

She knew that John was...John. An interesting man, a mixture of tough and tender, calculating and generous. He'd been one of a large family who'd had to struggle to survive. She had never met any of John's family, although he had grown up in southern California.

He'd been different, he told her once, and never mentioned it again, nor let her mention it. He'd been a poor kid who got lucky. Teachers saw he had talent. He wasn't bragging, he knew early what he had wanted and went after it. He always had a job. He won scholarships. Even a four-year one to the University of California at Berkeley.

Sarah knew John was headed to fame and fortune via architecture. He needs to be rich, she thought, more than he wants to be loved.

Is that wrong? she asked herself, viewing her image in the dressing-table mirror.

This day was special and she needed to look special. She'd chosen a three-piece outfit in tawny apricot. The short-cropped jacket and softly tailored skirt were of a silken fabric. Under the jacket she wore a handkerchief-linen blouse. Dyed-to-match cluny lace topped the collarband and was inserted down the front. The blouse was in a paler shade of the apricot and she knew it was very becoming to her blond coloring...and did wonders for her brown eyes.

She clipped on a pair of corduroy-ribbed gold earrings, then ran a manicured finger, its nail polished in Summer's Blush, over her dark naturally arched brows. Leaning close to the mirror, she removed a minuscule speck of powder from her long lashes. With one last touch of Joy behind each ear, she was ready.

No, she answered herself, looking straight into the

reflection of her golden-brown eyes. It wasn't wrong for John to want to be rich. To make his mark.

Isn't that what I want? she thought candidly. *To make my mark with my talents?* Being rich wasn't her top priority, but if it came with the territory... well, as Lara would say, terrific!

Excited about the day and its prospects, Sarah picked up her purse and briefcase and hurried out the door.

At work, she dealt with one crisis after another. It seemed that every client she had was experiencing some kind of difficulty. Except for the Benedict account.

John did call for lunch, his appointment suddenly canceled. But Sarah had, just minutes before, accepted a luncheon meeting with Jack Nelson of Bay Radio and TV. He'd come into her office wanting to discuss some spot announcements over a fast sandwich. It wouldn't be fair to change her mind just as they were about to walk out the door.

She thought that John sounded a bit annoyed. It angered her that while she was supposed to graciously accept his explanation that his day would be frantic, he felt she should cancel her business lunch. This was an irritating incongruity in their relationship. For all John's seemingly liberated attitude, he did have one set of "shoulds" for her and another for himself. But like all the other times when she encountered this inconsistency, Sarah pushed her reaction into the cupboard marked "later."

He waited just the barest fraction of a moment longer than necessary before he said, "Okay. I understand. I'll be free about five. Shall I pick you up?"

"No. Let me call you. Mr. Benedict is coming in sometime this afternoon with the photos I need for Evans, the printer, tomorrow. John, please excuse me. I've got to run."

Bryce arrived shortly before three. When Lara showed him into her office, it was as if an electric charge filled the room. He wore a navy blue blazer, gray flannel slacks, a crisp white shirt and a handsome tie of gray, dark blue and maroon stripes. To Sarah he looked sharp and clean, and the feeling of vitality he exuded was incredible. Under his arm he carried the portfolio of photographs he had reclaimed from Holcomb.

"Wonderful," Sarah exclaimed, when they had been spread out on her worktable. She stepped to the door of Richard's workroom and beckoned to him.

When he joined them, she said, "Bryce, Richard Wong. Richard, Bryce Benedict."

As the two men shook hands, Richard said, "Well, Mr. Benedict, I approve most heartily of your Recherché. Such a wine is long overdue." Then, with a wink at Sarah, he added, "Before a revolt is necessary."

Bryce and Sarah laughed. "I told Bryce what you said about the peasants' dire need." Then, indicating the photographs, she said, "Well, Richard, cast your honorable eye on these."

There were several five-by-seven photographs depicting the progression of the vineyard ripening for harvest. There were several smaller photographs of the actual grapes. The larger compositions were all mood pieces, shot in beautifully muted colors. The smaller photos, meant to be used as insets, were sharper in definition, bringing the focus to the grapes.

Bryce talked as he pointed out the changes. "The first bud break occurs in mid-March when the soft leaf unfolds on the vine. By May the fruit buds look like clusters of miniature grapes. In mid-June these blossom into grape flowers." He picked up the small photo showing the wreath of blossoms. "This flowering marks the critical stage in growing wine grapes. To develop a full crop, the vines must have ten to fourteen days of dry, moderately warm weather. Rain is a disaster...and so is extreme heat. Once the fruit sets, berries form quickly."

He worked his way through the photographs. "This occurs in mid-July when the vines stop growing and the fruit begins to mature. See," he pointed to a smaller photograph. "This purple tinge announces the grapes are ripening."

Sarah remembered that he'd said most of his ripen in early October.

The next two photographs he'd brought along were spectacular. One was of harvest, shot in early dawn as the sun blazed red and gold across the sky sending rays of lights across the vineyards where pickers harvested the vines.

The other photograph was shot at sundown after a November rain had colored the vineyards crimson and yellow.

"Because Benedict vineyards are old, we get strong color," Bryce said, obviously proud of the sweep of brilliant color catching the last bright light of the autumn sun.

"Very nice," Richard said. "They'll be quite effective." Then he added, "And your wine is excellent. It deserves a quality campaign, Mr. Benedict."

Sarah felt a warm glow toward the tall man as he looked pleased at Richard's praise. Then she heard him say, "Bryce. The promotion of this wine is becoming more than just an advertising campaign. Please call me Bryce."

He turned back to Sarah. "You said you'd like to get the final art to the printer today or tomorrow. Is there anything I can do to help?"

"Well, we can use an extra hand to help with the paste-up."

"Just show me where to hang my coat," he replied with a grin.

The remainder of the afternoon passed quickly. Richard left to get the copy typeset, Sarah and Bryce selected and arranged the photos. Bryce approved the wine bottle label master Richard had completed, and suggested they make the box label the same, simply larger.

Lara held all calls, leaving Sarah free to concentrate entirely on this all-important phase of the Recherché campaign.

At seven o'clock, Sarah sent both Lara and Richard home. The final art for the brochure was nearly done, and she insisted that she and Bryce could easily finish it up. Lara and Richard were both tired and only made token protestations that they'd be happy to stay longer.

A few minutes later, the roar of San Francisco's homebound traffic had faded and the lights of Union Square gleamed beyond the windows when there was a knock at the locked office door. Hurrying to open it, Sarah found John there looking very annoyed.

"I thought we had a dinner date," he said. "Don't you ever go home anymore? When you didn't call back, I assumed you'd left for the day. I called your place... but no Sarah. So I came to pick you up."

"Oh, John! I'm so sorry," Sarah exclaimed. "I meant to call you back. But I got so busy—"

"So I see," John interrupted, his eyes fixed on Bryce bent over the worktable in her office.

"This is Mr. Benedict of Benedict Winery," she explained, leading John into the office. "I'm doing the campaign for a new sparkling red wine he's bringing out this fall. It's a rush job."

"John Carr." He shook hands with Bryce briefly.

"I really must have this together for the printer

tomorrow," Sarah said to John. "I'm afraid dinner is out." She held her breath, willing him not to be too personal in front of Bryce. She gave him a smile. "Forgive me?"

"Of course." John leaned to kiss her cheek. Sarah caught a flicker of concern in Bryce's eyes.

"Look...don't let this interfere with your other engagements, Miss Montgomery," Bryce protested.

"Of course it has to interfere. Tomorrow morning is the *only* time Evans can give me. This can't wait," she insisted. "Both of you have to take my word for it."

"No problem," John said coolly. Sarah knew he was miffed, whether because she hadn't called or because of Bryce's presence she didn't know. If because of Bryce, it would be a new experience for John. Since John became the man in her life, she had never before been unavailable to him.

Walking him to the outer door, she said, "John... I *am* sorry." She considered suggesting that as soon as she finished, which should be in another hour, she call him. They could still have this evening. In truth, she waited for him to suggest that she do so. They'd spent many evenings making love while most of the city had dinner. They'd often dined late afterward.

But John said nothing, putting the burden on her. And from somewhere deep within, Sarah heard a voice say wait. You've understood that his clients, his schedule, his work must be given priority much of the time. This time, this overlapping of his schedule demands and your schedule demands are on a collision course. He must understand. Wait, that voice cautioned...insisted. She listened.

"There's still Hawaii?" he asked with an uncertain look.

Sarah sighed. "This is a very good opportunity for

Montgomery Advertising, John. I can't muff it. Have a safe trip."

"I'll be calling you," he said, and with a brief cool kiss he was gone.

"I feel like a rat," Bryce said when she returned. "I should have asked if you had anything else planned."

"Not a rat," Sarah reassured him with a smile. "A client with a rush job. And it was my idea, remember?"

They worked for another hour and Sarah knew she could finish in a short time in the morning. Sighing, she stood up. "It's good. I like it," she said to Bryce. "How about you?"

"I like it too. You're fantastic," he replied with a grin. "Let me take you to dinner now, since I've ruined your evening."

Sarah found herself offering to make an omelet or take one of her free-evening-gourmet-cooking dishes from the freezer and microwave it. "Thaddeus and I have much in common. We both like poetry and we both like cooking. Though he needn't look to his laurels as far as I'm concerned," she finished wryly.

"Another time, I hope," he said. "You've worked long enough and certainly hard enough for one day. You deserve to be wined and dined. Come on," he coaxed, stretching his long arms and legs as he leaned back in the chair. "We both deserve it."

Acquiescing, she showed him where he could tidy up. In her private bathroom, she exchanged her work smock for her suit jacket and applied fresh makeup.

When she came out, he was waiting, looking as clean and crisp as he had when he'd walked in earlier that afternoon. When she heard him repeat, "fantastic," there was no mistaking his meaning.

Her pulse accelerated and as she watched his hazel eyes glint beguilingly with flecks of gold, her fatigue miraculously vanished.

His charm was potent, she told herself.

Bryce's car was in the garage under Union Square. As they made their way there, he asked if she had a preference for dinner.

"I've been making decisions all day long. You decide."

"Do you like the Nob Hill restaurant? It's quiet. The food's good. They have an excellent trout baked in paper...all right with you?"

"Fine," Sarah agreed, wondering about reservations. She'd been concerned that they could just walk into Doro's, but they'd had no problem.

The Nob Hill restaurant was located in the prestigious Mark Hopkins Hotel. Sarah had been to the Top of the Mark cocktail lounge many times. It was a wonderful place to have a drink and watch the city lights from twenty floors up atop Nob Hill, but she hadn't dined there.

The maître d' greeted him by name. Getting a table was no problem.

Once seated, she looked around. The dining room was quiet, as Bryce had promised. It was also tastefully conservative. Solid, old money, tradition. Like Bryce Benedict.

Sarah compared this setting to that of Maxwell's Plum where she and John had dined last night. Maxwell's Plum reportedly had cost seven million dollars. It was not known for understated elegance. It was a wonderfully fun restaurant. Especially for tourists, who for the most part have nothing like it back home. John liked the new, the bold, the innovative. And while he certainly had good taste, she didn't think anyone would call John conservative.

But then, she thought, she wouldn't call Bryce

conservative either. A traditionalist, certainly, but from that kiss at Madrona she knew that within this outwardly controlled man a barely banked fire was ready to blaze.

Sarah looked across the table at him and saw that he was watching her. He smiled a lover's smile, slow and intimate, and held her gaze with his.

A tremulous shiver coursed through her... warning her, she wondered, or foretelling... what? A kind of joy that hones the thrilling edge of desire?

The waiter came to their table just then and broke the electric contact. As she responded to Bryce's questions—preference of soup, dressing for her salad, yes, she'd like to try the trout—she was, on another level of consciousness, trying to identify the feeling this man had evoked every time she was with him.

When she'd met John at Bebe McDonald's party, they had found each other attractive. He had wined her and dined her all over San Francisco, introducing her to his city. John was an interesting man to be with, a considerate escort and host—and a sensual lover. Until this man had walked into her office with fire in his eyes and wrath against Grant Holcomb in his heart, she'd been quite satisfied with her life.

But now, even as she lifted her glass of Benedict Chardonnay and sipped her favorite wine, she acknowledged there was something about this man that attracted her in a way that was absolutely threatening to her status quo.

After dinner, on their way to her apartment, it was obvious that Bryce was looking for a certain kind of shop. It was quite late, and on a Tuesday night most business establishments were closed. She was about to ask what he was looking for when he pulled to the curb and told her he'd be right back.

Two young men were changing the display in a florist-shop window. They kept shaking their heads at Bryce's insistent knocking until he reached into his pocket and took out his wallet. He held up a bill and one of the men shrugged and with a broad grin opened the door.

In just a minute Bryce was back with a huge bouquet of bronze chrysanthemums. "Flowers for a lovely lady," he said, thrusting them into her arms.

"My favorite. How did you know?"

"Two great minds...." He grinned and added, "Bronze chrysanthemums happened to be what they had."

When they reached her apartment, he said he'd help her carry in the bouquet, if she'd like. She looked at him, wanting to ask him in for a nightcap...remembering that look they'd exchanged at dinner and feeling again the same shiver of desire.

Decline, she told herself. Say it's late. Thank him for his help this afternoon. Thank him for a lovely dinner and for the flowers whose pungent aroma filled the space between them. Say good-night.

"Yes...I'd like that," she heard herself say instead. "Perhaps you'd like coffee before you head for the hills?"

"That would be nice." His voice had dropped a register.

Sarah knew he felt much the same as she did. She knew it with the same certainty that she knew the sun would rise in the east tomorrow morning.

In her apartment, she switched on soft lamplight. "I'll just be a minute," she said, taking the flowers and heading into the kitchen. There, she turned on the coffee maker, then took a deep bowl and filled it with water. Setting the bowl in a large Shaker basket, she arranged the bouquet.

A few minutes later, she took the flower arrangement along with the coffee tray into the living room.

When Bryce complimented her on the arrangement and the basket, she told him it was one of her favorite possessions, a gift from her mother. With a smile, she said, "Mom, though not of the Shaker persuasion, really appreciated the society's insistence on 'the meticulous care and management of temporal things.'"

"That has a nice ring to it, doesn't it? Care and management of temporal things,'" he repeated.

Inexplicably, she thought of Adam. Of the fleeting young years of the little boy. She wondered if Bryce did also.

"Interesting, this room." He looked admiringly around her living room. "Tells a lot about you. Nice mixture of eclectic and Sarah Montgomery." As he handed her the coffee he had poured, he asked if her mother combined a career and homemaking.

"No," Sarah said. "She loves being home. My father loves her being home. My brother, sister and I selfishly enjoyed it." Then, deciding the conversation was taking a direction best avoided, she drew him to the window. The night was clear, they could see the bright lights of downtown and the Bay Bridge, a necklace of gleaming lights strung across the bay.

"Quite a view you have."

"It is beautiful, isn't it? I love it." She sipped her coffee, then said, "Of course you have quite a view yourself. Your own hills, private forest...."

"Yes," he agreed, watching her, "but the view here is very beautiful." His voice was soft and husky.

Aware of how intensely he was looking at her, Sarah suddenly felt anxious. "I don't usually invite clients home...even after *they* buy dinner. I—"

"It's just me," Bryce said, looking at her. "Women trust me...women, children and dogs. I'm definitely the dependable type." His tone was light, his mouth curved in a grin, but his eyes did not smile. A wariness came into them, dulling the sparkle and darkening the golden hazel. They held hurt and loneliness.

Sarah caught her breath. She was sure this man had no idea how appealing his quiet strength could be. Quickly she stood up, and going to the tape deck, switched it on.

"More Mozart," she said lightly.

"I think he just became my favorite composer," Bryce said quietly. "Sarah...Saturday night was one of the better nights of my life."

Don't, Sarah thought, don't let's talk about it. *I can't admit how deeply my emotions were stirred that night.* Just being there in the moonlight with him—his hand holding hers—and Mozart filling the summer air.

"Sarah?" He took the coffee cup from her and set it on a table. His big hands clasped her shoulders and drew her toward him. Sarah found she was trembling. Afraid. Eager. Knowing what was happening was as inevitable as sunrise.

Held in his embrace, Sarah felt his lips caress her eyelids, her temple, her ear. A tremor shook her body as he drew her closer, his strong muscular body pressed against hers. With a sigh, she yielded to his embrace, her arms reached around his neck to draw his mouth down to hers. Her whole being tingled, glowed, waited for the touch of his lips on her own.

His mouth took hers, gentle at first, arousing, then probing, exploring hers. Stunned by the fierce reaction within her, Sarah found herself responding ravenously. All her senses flaming, Sarah yearned for this kiss to go on and on. Then, as though shaken by his own emotion, Bryce held her away from him, looking deep into her eyes. The only sound in the room was their ragged breathing in concert with one another.

His eyes were dark with emotion. "I think I just blew my dependable image," he said wryly, still holding her, still watching her.

Struggling to even out her breathing and to control her feelings, Sarah murmured, "I'm afraid so."

"Sarah?" She was aware of the wariness that had returned to his eyes. They also questioned.

"You'd better go, Bryce. It's getting late." In spite of her effort, she heard a quivering in her voice.

"It's not that late...." He waited.

Things were moving too fast and in a direction she wasn't prepared for. All through dinner, she'd been aware of his special attraction...speculated upon it. Every time they were in each other's company it was as if a magnet was drawing the two of them together. And she had known this kiss would happen. Had wanted it to happen. Now she had to stop and reorganize things. Without looking at them, she saw in her mind's eye the nested Shaker boxes on the bookshelf..."meticulous care and management of temporal things."

This campaign to launch Recherché was a temporal affair.

She stepped away from Bryce and picked up her cup again. "Your Chardonnay keeps going to my head, I think," she said, trying for the light touch. "Saturday night...." She paused, took a sip of coffee, then tried again. "Tonight...what I'm trying to say, Bryce, is that for some reason I keep forgetting you're my client. I never mix business and—"

"Are you engaged to John Carr?"

The question was abrupt and to the point. Bryce's

tone was no-nonsense, his manner forthright as he waited for her answer. He was asking in plain terms if she was available or if she was taken.

She had a sudden profound feeling that everything depended on her answer. If she said, "I belong to John," Bryce would back off. She knew that as surely as if he'd said so. But if she indicated that the subject was open to question, he would pursue her. And she'd already gotten the strong impression that he was a man who got what he went after.

As she hesitated, he continued, "Carr certainly was acting like he had a proprietary interest in you. So, I repeat—are you engaged?"

"No," Sarah admitted reluctantly, with a feeling that she was burning her bridges. "I'm not engaged."

She didn't elaborate on John's behavior or their relationship. She didn't have to.

Bryce's lips curved slightly in the merest ghost of a smile. But there was a light in his eyes that was unmistakable and that warmed Sarah's heart.

After a long silence, he looked slowly around the room. "You live here alone, don't you?" he asked.

"Obviously. No one else lives here." She felt defensive and she didn't like that. Of course, she had no one but herself to blame for this situation. Part of her wanted to be angry with him. The other part of her wanted him to stop talking and take her in his arms again.

Desire and discretion warred within her. It was, she thought, like being on the pointed peak of a rock. When climbing, you can use the point to thrust yourself upward, or to steady yourself as you descend. But you cannot balance there very long.

Taking a deep breath, Sarah said, "Bryce, you're right about John. I'm not exactly free."

"You're not married, engaged or living together,"

he responded, his voice husky with the same warring emotions she was battling within herself. "Maybe you're not exactly free, but you're not entirely taken either."

He picked up his coffee cup and finished the last drop. Then he set the cup down. And with the same confidence that secured them a table without reservations, he placed a hand on each of her shoulders and held her tightly for a moment. He dropped a light kiss on her lips, a teasing reminder of what they'd experienced before, then said good-night.

For a long time, Sarah stood looking out at the city lights. The scent of the chrysanthemums was strong. She thought of her mother—her lovely, bright, talented mother who spent her days serving one man, her family, her community...never stretching beyond those boundaries.

What is the matter with me? she asked herself. *Bryce Benedict is not the kind of man I want to be involved with. He would demand too much of me, take too much of my hard-won freedom. I don't want my neat, well-ordered life disrupted.*

Besides, she argued with herself, *there's John.* His constant traveling was responsible for the hiatus in their relationship.

But once more, her mother's face superimposed itself on her thoughts. Sarah envisioned that face as she had seen it a thousand times...turning from her husband's greeting kiss, a smile on her lips, her eyes shining with love.

Rising, Sarah moved to the bar and poured a small glass of brandy. As she drank it, she looked out the window into the night. She imagined Bryce crossing the Golden Gate Bridge, heading north to Madrona. She felt again his ardent strength as his arms held her in that warm embrace...and tasted again his mouth sweet with passion.

Finishing the last of the brandy, she went to bed. But as she lay there she still enjoyed a warmth deep inside that she knew did not come from the brandy. Nor from thinking of John, who should have shared her bed this night.

THE DRIVE WAS SO FAMILIAR, even in the dark, that Bryce felt he could almost make it with his eyes closed. That meant that his mind was free to wander over the events of the day. And it had certainly been an interesting day.

It had been a long time since he'd pursued a woman as he was pursuing Sarah. Normally it was the other way around. He wasn't vain, but he was realistic enough to know that he was a catch—single, financially secure, attractive. An object of interest to any marriage-minded or affair-minded woman. For months after his divorce, he'd dated a dizzying number of women to bolster his shattered ego. That had quickly paled. He'd settled into a comfortable routine of dating one woman at a time. But the relationships did not last because Bryce made it clear he would never offer marriage—and sooner or later that was what most women wanted.

Not Sarah, a voice inside him remarked acidly. She couldn't hide the fact that she was as attracted to him as he was to her, but she certainly fought that attraction. She didn't want to get involved with him, and didn't feel a need for marriage—to Bryce or anyone.

Was that it, he wondered. Was his ego piqued by the challenge of a woman who made it clear she wasn't available?

But even as the thought crossed his mind, he knew it wasn't true. His period of bedding women as ego-gratification was an aberration—it wasn't his true nature.

So what *is* the attraction, he asked himself again. She's pretty but not spectacularly so. Bright and charming, but not an alluring femme fatale. In fact, if anything, she's rather wholesome and sweet.

Then he remembered that kiss wasn't sweet—it was passionate and uninhibited. This was no nice girl but a multifaceted woman with a seductive sexuality. An exciting woman who stirred his interest as no woman had done in a long while.

He liked everything about her—the clothes she wore, her long silky blond hair, her homey charming apartment. He liked the honest, straightforward way she did business....

Suddenly his musing came to an abrupt halt. Her business. She was definitely a businesswoman, ambitious and independent. She wasn't looking for a husband to care for or a child—especially another woman's child—to raise. John Carr was probably exactly what she wanted—a man as career-oriented as she, who made no demands on her.

In a flash, Bryce realized he and Sarah were absolutely mismatched. Wrong for each other. Period.

That realization should have ended his attraction to her, he knew. But it didn't. When he finally pulled into the driveway at Madrona, he was still thinking of her—and remembering that kiss.

5

IT WAS STILL QUITE EARLY when Sarah reached the Sonoma turnoff. Checking her watch, she was surprised to see she still had an hour and a half before her appointment with Bryce.

Good heavens, she wondered, *did I hurry?*

Familiar now with the area, she knew how long it would take to reach Madrona. She'd been waiting some time just to drive around. In the years she'd lived in San Francisco, she'd visited many of the famous wineries. Buena Vista. And Sebastiani, located right in Sonoma. She loved their spicy Gewürztraminer, especially with homemade vanilla ice cream and a crisp cookie for dessert.

She cut east to pick up the Silverado Trail, which paralleled the main highway through the area where most of the well-known wineries—Christian Brothers, Charles Krug, Inglenook—were situated.

Perhaps, she thought, if Bryce's new wine and the ad campaign were equally successful, Benedict Winery would become as well-known.

The road she drove followed the dips and curves of the vineyards. She'd read that more than one hundred wineries succeed in this verdant, often dramatic watershed.

Suddenly Sarah thought of Faribault. It too was a green and beautiful place to live. Remembering Bryce's choice of chrysanthemums that evening, she smiled. He'd have been surprised if she'd told him

"Mums in Minnesota" was an annual flower show at home. Two great minds, he'd joked. Indeed.

Bryce. Just thinking about him made her shiver in a way that had nothing to do with the coolness of the morning. For most of the past week, she'd managed to put him out of her mind, except following one brief phone conversation between them. She had worked long hours and spoken over the telephone several times to John.

While she was in San Francisco, John and their relationship dominated her thoughts. Yet the moment she crossed the Golden Gate Bridge, she'd begun to think of Bryce. And now, as before when she'd been here, she thought of Faribault. She knew it wasn't just the place that made her think of home. It was the people too. Bryce, Adam, and Thaddeus—all touched something deep within her.

Determined to put these disturbing thoughts from her mind, she rolled down the window and let the crisp breeze caress her face and toss her golden hair. On this glorious late-August morning, the scenery was delightfully picturesque. Handsome moss-roofed farmhouses with wide wraparound verandahs and weather vanes atop ornate cupolas, red-tile roofed Spanish haciendas, châteaus of native stone, shared the valley and hillsides with other plain or spectacular winery buildings.

At Oakville Road she turned west and drove up the mountain to a panoramic spot at the crest of the Mayacamus Range. She pulled over and stopped. On one side was the Napa Valley, and on the other, the Valley of the Moon.

She and John had picnicked here last year. It'd been spring, and yellow mustard filled in the bare vineyards. Pink plum trees lined country roads and blue lupine was everywhere. They'd spoken about how beautiful it was, picture-postcard pretty. She'd talked about the greenness reminding her of her home, telling him that Faribault lay on a terrace between two rivers and that the city spread over the slopes to the summit of high bluffs. She'd said for just a moment, she'd felt a pang of homesickness.

John had said that he came from a place that was dreary and ugly and that he never expected to lay eyes on it again.

Now looking at the vineyards in full leaf with the grapes beginning to mature, checkerboarding the valley and hills, Sarah could easily understand why Bryce, unlike his father, would never consider leaving here.

She was doing it again, she thought irritably. Letting him invade her thoughts, as if she had nothing better to think of.

She released the brake and began her descent. She tried to concentrate on business—Bay Radio and TV was already pleased with her work; an old client, L'Danseuse, a dance and exercise studio, would be needing a new campaign soon.

But as she drew closer and closer to Madrona, it became impossible to concentrate on anything other than seeing Bryce again. She felt a rising excitement that she was loath to analyze.

As she drove up in front of Madrona, she saw Adam racing around the side of the house, followed by two dogs. One, a full-grown German Shepherd, was on a leash. Sarah stepped from the car, but stayed behind the open door. She waved and called cheerfully, ''Hello.''

Adam stopped abruptly, clearly surprised to see her. The wariness Sarah had noticed on her previous visit was very much in evidence. On top of that, she knew, he was probably still piqued at her previous abrupt departure.

She would have to make friends with him all over
again. But she'd come prepared to do just that.

Sarah waited until Adam and the dogs began to
walk toward her. When he was within easy speaking
distance, he stopped. The big dog, obviously well
trained in protecting his young master, watched
Sarah warily, as did Adam. Then Adam tugged at
the leash and said, "It's okay, Rex." The big dog sat
back on his haunches. The other dog, a feisty little
terrier, immediately ran up to Sarah and began
dancing around happily.

Well, Sarah thought wryly, this has to be Pancho.
At least he doesn't hold a grudge.

She walked to Adam and crouched down so she
could look him straight in the eye. "It's nice to see
you again, Adam," Sarah began.

He nodded, saying nothing. His eyes looked everywhere but at her.

Sarah continued, "I've brought you something.
Would you like to see it?"

Immediately his small face lit with excitement at
the prospect of a surprise. He nodded, and Sarah
opened her briefcase. From it she took out a book; an
old, carefully cared for copy of *Paul Bunyan*.

Handing it to Adam, she explained, "It's all about
a great lumberman and his blue ox, Babe. I got this
when I was just about your age and enjoyed it very
much. I hope you will too."

"I can keep it?" Adam asked, meeting her look for
the first time.

Sarah smiled. "Yes. You can keep it. It's yours."

Taking the book, he began turning the pages ea-
gerly. Then, suddenly remembering his manners, he
said, "Thank you, Sarah."

"You're quite welcome, Adam. Now then, is your
father inside?"

"Yes."

"Could you take me to him, please?"

"Sure." He took the leash off Rex, then asked, "Will you be here a long time?"

Sarah hesitated. She knew what he meant—would she leave suddenly again, going in and out of his life unpredictably? Finally, she answered, "I'll be leaving this afternoon. But I'll make sure I see you before I go."

"Will you come back again?"

Sarah met those questioning hazel eyes and saw the same guarded expression she'd seen in his father's, blanking out friendliness. "Yes," she promised, resisting a sudden desire to pull this child into her arms. "I'll be back."

This seemed to mollify him, and he led her into the house, holding her hand with his much smaller one. The feel of that little hand tugging hers tugged at her heart, as well. She felt deeply touched and near tears. Thus, a moment later when she came face to face with Bryce, instead of being cool and collected as she had planned, she felt vulnerable and susceptible.

He was standing near the fireplace in the living room. Since last seeing him in San Francisco, she'd told herself her memory had exaggerated his appeal. She thought that when she saw him again, she'd realize he was a fairly attractive man, nothing more. Certainly no competition for John who held the key to her heart. This demanding, exacting, old-fashioned man could be no threat.

Now she looked at him. He was dressed casually in jeans and a light blue shirt open at the throat, the blue complementing his sun-bronzed skin and light brown hair. He looked crisply clean and outdoorsy—his boots polished, his shirt-sleeves rolled above his elbows. His arms were tanned and muscular.

As she met the look in those greenish-brown eyes
tinged with gold, all her determined resistance vanished. She was glad she'd worn her favorite summer
dress. It was straw-colored, which was very becoming to her brown-eyed blondness. The shade looked
like ripened golden grain. Crisp linen, it fit like a
dream. It was worth every outrageous dollar it had
cost. Some dresses made a woman *feel* like a woman;
this was such a dress. The appreciation in his eyes
told her so as he looked at her—momentarily taking
in the total picture, stopping a moment on the string
of amber beads she wore, then coming back to look
directly into her eyes. Then he smiled, a sweet welcoming smile.

He was *much* more than just another attractive
man. Without being precisely handsome, he was
nevertheless devastatingly attractive and com-
pelling. She not only didn't feel disappointed in him,
she felt exhilarated just being with him.

She noticed the perfect fit of his jeans on his slim
hips and sinewy thighs, the way the shirt stretched
tautly over his broad, well-muscled shoulders and
chest.

Adam ran ahead of her to his father. "Look, dad,"
he said, "Sarah brought me a book."

Watching him, Sarah noticed that his small body,
clad in jeans and a T-shirt, was much like his
father's; his tiny shoulders would one day be broad,
his short legs would be long.

Looking back up at Bryce, Sarah could see that he
felt just as happy to see her as she felt to see him.

"You must have left the city early. I didn't expect
you for another hour." He took the book that Adam
held up to him, looked at its title and handed it back
to the boy. "That's very nice, Adam. You'll like that
story."

"It was Sarah's book. When she was little like

me." Adam was not yet ready to relinquish his father's attention.

"That was certainly kind of Sarah," he said, looking at her over Adam. "Well, Sarah, we're both delighted that you're here."

"There's a great deal of work to go over," she said, determined to get the conversation back on track. "I thought you'd like to get through it so you could get other things done today."

"Actually, I've set aside my entire day for you," he replied. His eyes had a mischievous glint, and Sarah sensed that he didn't plan to spend the whole day working. Her own plans didn't include a repetition of that kiss that had sent her senses reeling. But she didn't know how to make that clear in a subtle way, so she remained silent.

Bryce continued, "We don't get terribly busy until harvest. Then it's a madhouse—sixteen-hour days, going at a frantic pace, a million and one things to do and not enough time to do them."

Sarah shook her head and quipped, "It's a good thing harvest only comes once a year."

He smiled again. The way his smile softened his strong features did something funny to Sarah's heart.

"We get used to it. And it does have its rewards." Turning to Adam, he said, "Sarah and I will be working in my office for a while. Why don't you find Thaddeus and ask him to prepare a special lunch?"

Adam's face brightened. "How about hot dogs with cheese?"

Bryce laughed. "Let's leave the choice up to Thaddeus. Sarah might not share your taste."

As Adam ran from the room, Sarah said, "Actually, I love hot dogs. Especially with cheese."

In his office, Bryce continued teasing. "Hot dogs!

What were we doing with trout baked in paper...?"
His eyes were bright with obvious pleasure in the
conversation.

"We were having a well-deserved, restful dinner,
thank you," she said, enjoying the banter. "Sometime we must take Adam to the Nobel Frankfurter.
Have you ever had one of *their* hot dogs?" she suggested before it occurred to her that she was being
presumptuous.

"I'm right. You *do* have eclectic tastes."

"Really. Perhaps that's because I've made some
moves. My father enjoyed meat and potatoes served
with gravy, two vegetables, a salad and dessert. My
mother enjoyed pleasing my father. She didn't serve
many enchilada casseroles. After college, when I was
on my own, I favored fast foods. When I moved to
San Francisco...well, my culinary tastes and skills
broadened considerably." She paused, then finished,
"But that change was brought about as much by
time—where my head was—as by place."

Thinking now of John and his sophisticated life-
style and friends, she realized that her tastes had
been broadened in more ways than one. She prided
herself on being chic and knowledgeable, on being
able to fit in smoothly in John's milieu. She could
order from a menu in a French restaurant without
prompting a condescending smirk from the waiter.
And she could talk with sincere enthusiasm about
the latest plays, novels and foreign films. But she
could do these things before she knew John. It was
just that to him they were important things to
know.

To her discomfort, she caught Bryce watching her
closely. She had the unnerving sensation that he was
reading her mind. Determined to put things back on
an impersonal footing, she continued, "Here are the
storyboards for the radio and TV commercials and

copies of the ads as they'll appear in magazines and newspapers."

She laid the material out on his desk, then took a seat in the chair opposite.

As Bryce sat down in the high-backed leather chair behind his desk and slowly perused the material, she watched him. She was more than a little concerned about his reaction. It would be difficult to make major changes at this late stage. And if he really disliked it, if he decided to fire her as he had Holcomb....

Don't be ridiculous, she told herself. Her work was awfully good. He'd said so only a week before. If he had any sense at all he'd see that the whole campaign was shaping up very well, indeed. And if he did fire her, it wouldn't be the first time she lost a client.

But the problem, as she well knew, was that she didn't just see him as a client any longer.

Glancing up at Sarah, Bryce caught her worried frown. Smiling reassuringly, he said, "I like it. *Very* much."

She felt intense relief wash over her.

He continued, "There are just a few points I'd like to go over with you. The number of spots on network television, their cost, etcetera."

For the next hour they discussed the ad campaign in detail. Sarah was following through on Holcomb's planned media blitz involving radio, television, newspaper and magazine advertising. It was timed to begin when the first shipments of the wine were due to reach the stores—at the same time as the party premiering the wine in October.

Sarah had just finished explaining the estimated cost of the series of commercials planned for TV, when Adam came bouncing into the room.

"Thaddeus says lunch's ready!" he announced.

It was, as before, delicious. Thaddeus was clearly glad to see Sarah again. As they ate fresh spinach salad with a tart dressing, followed by shrimp crepes in white sauce, he talked to Sarah about the city.

"I love San Francisco—the restaurants, museums...." His voice trailed off wistfully.

Bryce grinned. "Yet every time you come back from there, you say how good it is to be home, away from the noise, the crowds, the traffic."

Thaddeus laughed ruefully. "It's true. I couldn't *live* there." Then, remembering that he might have offended Sarah, who *did* live in the city, he added, "Not that it couldn't be pleasant. I'm afraid I've just gotten spoiled by the peace and quiet of Madrona."

There was a time when the last thing Sarah wanted was the rural virtues of peace and quiet; when she longed for the noise and bustle and excitement of a cosmopolitan city. However, she could understand Thaddeus's love of Madrona. It was easy to fall in love with this beautiful place.

Aloud, she said, "You're lucky, Thaddeus. The place where you make your living is also a pleasant place to live. Most of us aren't that fortunate. I have to work in a fairly large city because of the nature of my job. I'm just glad I get to live in a city as marvelous as San Francisco."

"But you're a country girl," Bryce interjected. "Don't you miss it?"

There was an intensity about the question that caught Sarah off guard. He was digging at something and she wasn't entirely sure what it was.

She answered slowly, "I wasn't actually a Minnesota farm girl, despite my wisecrack to the contrary the first time we met. Faribault is small but not unsophisticated. It's not very far from Minneapolis. My father still teaches at Shattuck, a prep school that's highly regarded." Smiling, she finished, "However,

I did spend summers at my grandfather's farm in the Red River Valley.''

"The Red River Valley?'' Bryce repeated, curious. "There's an old song about that place... 'from this valley they say you are going...'''

"I'm surprised that song is in your repertoire,'' Sarah interrupted with a laugh. "I can relate to your concern for rain and sun and no frost. The summer I was seventeen I watched a black cloud boil across the sky and, within minutes, hailstones as big as golf balls literally beat the grain lifeless the day before it was to be harvested.''

"That happens,'' Bryce said. Then, before anyone else could comment, he referred again to the song. "Everyone knows that song. It's a wonderful piece of Americana.'' He reached over to smooth his hand across Adam's head. "I'll teach it to you someday,'' he told his son. "It ends with 'and the cowboy who loved you so true.'''

"Did a cowboy love you, Sarah?'' Adam's candor delighted the three adults.

"'Fraid not. My grandfather grew wheat. He didn't raise cattle.'' Sarah spoke to Adam, but her glance strayed and her brown eyes met Bryce's and she watched that interesting marbling of green, gold and brown. It was as if the emotion he was experiencing acted as a catalytic agent and stirred the colors in concert with his feelings. The dancing glints of gold reflected a deeply felt happiness.

A mouth can smile, Sarah knew, even when sad. But eyes cannot express that dancing light when it doesn't come from within.

His look was unmistakable. Memories of that stolen kiss flooded her senses.

Anxious to change the subject, Sarah said, "Apropos to my not being a farm girl, I really do consider myself a career woman, you know. And in some ways, at least, that has to take precedence over my love of nature."

At that moment, the telephone rang. Thaddeus left the table to answer it, then returned quickly.

"It's a problem at the winery," he told Bryce. "Not enough glue on the labels. They won't stick properly."

"Hell," Bryce muttered under his breath. He didn't want to leave, but had no choice. Rising, he said to Sarah, "I'll try to make this as quick as possible. There are still some things I'd like to discuss with you about the ad campaign. Will you excuse me for a few minutes?"

"Of course."

Turning to Adam, Bryce asked, "Will you keep Sarah company while I'm gone?"

Adam was clearly pleased to be given such an adult reponsibility. "Sure."

When Bryce had gone and Thaddeus was busy with the dishes, Adam led Sarah into his bedroom. It was a small boy's vision of paradise—the walls were decorated with bold graphics in bright circus colors, foam cushions in a variety of shapes, a bed shaped like a race car. In a corner, on a large raised platform, was an electric train. The track wound through papier-mâché mountain tunnels and plastic fir trees.

Sarah asked Adam to show her how the train worked, and he happily complied. For half an hour they played with the fascinating toy, both enjoying it immensely. Sarah realized she'd finally won back Adam's friendship completely when he offered to let her pull the switches that controlled the track.

"I love your train, Adam. Did your father give it to you?"

"No, my mother did," he said matter-of-factly.

With a jolt, Sarah was reminded of the woman

who had turned her back on this child, on Bryce and on Madrona. Looking at Adam's angelic face, the perfect features lit with intense amusement as he played with the train, she wondered about this nameless woman.

She was obviously bright and ambitious, judging by her career. And probably pretty as well, since Adam was a beautiful child. How on earth could she have left her husband and child, Sarah wondered.

Does she sleep well at night, knowing that her son is thousands of miles away, knowing that she's missing the years when he's growing and constantly changing?

And Bryce—does she miss him? Does she care that she hardened his heart by her abandonment?

For a moment, Sarah felt not only confusion but anger at this selfish woman.

But reason told her that the woman might not have been entirely selfish. It may well have been extremely difficult for her to leave Adam. The gift of the train—a gift that would remind Adam of her every time he played with it—was evidence of caring. Perhaps, Sarah admitted grudgingly, she left Adam only because she knew he would be happier at Madrona with Bryce than in Africa on an isolated dig with her. Was she, perhaps, selfless rather than selfish? After all, she had left to pursue a career, presumably one she cared deeply about. She had to go where that career took her, or give it up. Sarah had just said as much at lunch about her own work.

She wasn't behaving any differently, Sarah thought. She just hadn't abandoned a husband and child in the process. But therein lay the difference. Sarah had left Minnesota when it became apparent to her that she was *the someone* Kenny Olson wanted to find. And while he was a very special person, the feeling was not reciprocated.

She knew she could never leave a child—or a man like Bryce—once she had made a commitment to him. She would give up her career, if such a choice had to be made. But she would resent it deeply, she feared. In that situation there were no easy answers.

Does it have to come to that, she wondered. Do women always have to make a choice? Can't we have it all, as Lara so optimistically puts it? She thought of John, who encouraged her career, who genuinely seemed to want her to be as successful as she could be. On the other hand, he said nothing of marriage and children.

"Sarah! I asked you a question."

Startled, Sarah realized Adam had been speaking to her and she had been lost in thought.

"I'm sorry. What was your question?"

"I said, what work do you do with my dad?"

In simple terms that Adam could grasp, Sarah explained her job and what she hoped to do for his father's wine.

"When I'm big, I can drink wine," he announced.

Sarah smiled. "That won't be too long. You seem to have grown just since I saw you last."

He beamed, pleased.

Sarah suggested that they go out onto the deck and Adam happily agreed. They were standing there, looking out over the Madrona vineyards, when Bryce returned.

Bryce told Adam it was time for his nap, and after a ritual argument, Adam finally left. When the child had gone, Bryce walked over to the railing where Sarah stood.

"I'm sorry I was gone so long. It was a complicated problem."

"Don't apologize. Adam and I had a marvelous time. He showed me his train."

As soon as she said it, Sarah was afraid she'd

made a faux pas. The train would only remind Bryce of the woman who gave it to Adam, the woman who had rejected both of them. Fortunately, Bryce didn't seem overly touchy on the subject. He merely nodded.

Even so, Sarah decided to steer the conversation in a neutral direction. "Why don't we finish going over that material now," she suggested.

"Okay."

An hour later, they had finished the work. As Sarah gathered the papers together and put them in her briefcase, Bryce watched her with a hint of amusement in his hazel eyes.

"So, you're rushing back to the city?" he asked.

Meeting his look, she responded evenly, "Not rushing exactly. But my work here is done."

"Why don't you stay for dinner? Adam and Thaddeus would like it." He added in a slightly huskier tone, "And so would I."

This time she couldn't quite meet his look. "I'm afraid I do have to be going."

It was true, in a way. She *had* to go, because to stay would be to risk a repeat performance of that romantic interlude that still haunted her.

Rising, she finished in her best woman-executive tone, "I'll have some more material for you to go over in a week or two. Will you be in the city then?"

He shook his head. "I don't think so. I hate to inconvenience you, but could you come here again?"

She hesitated. She wanted to say, *It's no inconvenience, I love coming here.* Instead, she replied, "No problem. It's all part of the service."

He smiled warmly, and to her chagrin, her heart turned over.

Bryce walked with her to her car, where Sarah found a small bunch of orange poppies mingled with tufts of grass and a slender-stemmed weed ly-

ing on her front seat. Sarah knew immediately
where they had come from, though there was no
Adam in sight.

Turning to Bryce, she said, "Well, you Benedict
men certainly know how to treat a lady. First, you
wine and dine me at one of the city's best restaurants, and now flowers."

Bryce's look had grown more intimate. "Like
father, like son. Adam's smitten with you too."

Having absolutely no idea how to reply to that,
Sarah merely swallowed hard and got into her car.
As she turned the key in the ignition and glanced
up, she saw that Adam had come out onto the front
steps and was sitting with the Paul Bunyan book on
his knees. She smiled at him and waved. This time,
he waved back at her—tentatively.

Bryce bent down across the open window. "He's
wary—and with good cause."

And so should I be, Sarah thought.

Later, as she drove back down the road she'd
come up only hours earlier, she thought of Bryce. It
was very disturbing to realize that the attraction
she'd felt for him earlier wasn't just a passing fancy.
What did that say about her relationship with John?

She wasn't sure she wanted to know the answer to
that question.

6

Sᴀʀᴀʜ ᴡᴀʟᴋᴇᴅ ɪɴᴛᴏ ᴛʜᴇ ᴏꜰꜰɪᴄᴇ bright and early Monday morning. As soon as she saw Lara's face, her good humor disappeared. "What's wrong?" she asked.

Not quite meeting her look, Lara answered with a forced cheerfulness, "Nothing."

"But you look awful." Sarah added with an apologetic smile, "Sorry. I mean, you look like something awful has happened."

"No. I guess I just stayed up too late last night. There was a good movie on ᴛᴠ and I went to bed much later than usual."

Sarah looked at Lara intently. The girl's eyes were red-rimmed and swollen—perhaps from a late night. And perhaps from crying. But Sarah didn't want to force Lara to talk about a problem if there was one. She valued her own privacy too much to invade someone else's.

But as the morning wore on, she became increasingly concerned about Lara. The girl was normally effervescent and cheerful, a Pollyanna if ever there was one. Yet today she was quiet and subdued. None of Sarah's comments rated Lara's proverbial, "terrific!" And when she thought no one was looking, her blue eyes took on a crushed look.

At noon, Sarah went into the rest room down the hall to freshen her hair and makeup before going out to lunch. She found Lara in there, crying softly to herself.

That does it, she thought. Whether she wants it or not, Lara obviously needs help.

"Come on," Sarah insisted. "I'm taking you to lunch."

"But the office..." Lara began through her sniffles.

"We'll just lock the door. I'm not expecting anyone till this afternoon."

A few minutes later, the two young women sat at a patio table under the jaunty blue awning of the Chestnut Street Grill in the Marina district. Sarah ordered sandwiches made of melted cheddar cheese, bacon and tomato for both of them.

Resting her elbows on the table and cupping her chin in her hands, Sarah began, "I don't want to be nosy. But you seem to have a serious problem. I want to help, if I can."

Lara smiled gratefully. Sarah realized that the poor girl had been dying for someone to insist that she unburden herself.

In a rush of jumbled words mingled with tears, Lara explained that her boyfriend of two years, Chuck, had walked out on her last night.

"Why? What happened?" Sarah asked.

Lara shook her head helplessly. "Nothing. Absolutely nothing."

"But there must have been *something*."

"You'd think so, wouldn't you? You'd think a man wouldn't throw away two years for no reason at all. But he did."

"What did he say?"

Lara took a sip of iced tea, then replied, "He came over to my place. We were supposed to go out to dinner. Instead, he told me he wanted to break it off. Not just take a break from each other, or go out with other women. But break it off entirely. Forever."

"Didn't he give you a reason?"

"I asked, of course." Lara smiled ruefully. She was beginning to get her emotions in hand now. "He just said he didn't want a serious relationship. He felt we were getting too close. Oh, Sarah, how can you get *too* close?"

Sarah didn't reply. She knew Lara didn't really expect an answer.

Lara continued, "For two years our relationship has grown better and better. We enjoyed each other's company and never had a fight. I thought we wanted the same things out of life. I'm only twenty-one and he's twenty-four, so I knew it was a little too early to talk about marriage. But I assumed someday...." Her voice trailed off helplessly.

For a long moment, Sarah said nothing. She wasn't as shocked by Chuck's attitude as Lara was. She'd heard a few of her friends complain about the same thing. When they got too close to a man, when sheer pleasure in each other's company turned into love and the logical next step was commitment—the men panicked and ran. Emotional intimacy, apparently, was a frightening thing to some men.

Sarah found herself thinking of John. Theirs was a perfect relationship—as long as Sarah didn't try to get too close. There was a duality about him that intimidated her. At the same time that he made it clear she was the main woman in his life, he was careful to maintain a boundary between them. Thus, Sarah was afraid to push for that complete intimacy that she knew must be the cornerstone of any lasting relationship.

Looking at Lara, Sarah realized that the poor girl was still too young to realize how complicated love could be. She didn't understand how love could be broken just as it was beginning to bloom.

Lara said softly, in a lost-little-girl voice, "I never pressured him at all. Things were so good between us, I thought it wasn't necessary to ask about the future. The future seemed certain."

What can I say to her, Sarah wondered, feeling helpless in the face of Lara's abject misery. Could she be honest, tell Lara she was better off without Chuck if he couldn't handle closeness? She knew Lara didn't want to hear that. Lara was hurt and disillusioned and didn't understand why life wasn't going the way she expected it to go. Unfortunately, Sarah thought, it wasn't the last time Lara's trust would probably be betrayed.

The waiter brought the thick delicious-looking sandwiches, and for a moment the women paused to eat. Lara's youth showed in the fact that her appetite wasn't affected by her emotional state. If anything, she was even hungrier than usual. Sarah couldn't help being a little amused by that ability to bounce back from disaster. No matter how devastated Lara might feel, at twenty-one she still had that youthful determination that life must go the way she wanted—if not today, then surely tomorrow.

At twenty-nine, Sarah knew that life was perfectly capable of going sour not once, but over and over again.

When she had finished her sandwich and sat quietly sipping the iced tea, Lara asked tentatively, "Sarah... what do you think I should do?"

"About Chuck?"

"Yeah."

Sarah paused. May as well be blunt, she told herself. She cared too much about Lara to foist empty platitudes on her. "I don't think there's anything you can do about Chuck. He has to find the courage within himself to make a commitment. If he can't do that...." She hesitated, then finished, "You can't change him. You can only change yourself. Do whatever you can to get over him. Be good to yourself, pamper yourself a little. Fill your time with activities you enjoy. Keep busy, don't stay at home moping. And hope that it won't take too long to get over him."

It wasn't what Lara wanted to hear, Sarah knew. But it was the truth.

Lara sighed. "Easier said than done," she quipped in a brave attempt at her old humor. Her blue eyes swam with unshed tears.

Sarah smiled. "I know."

Lara said pensively, "You're so lucky. You have it all."

"What exactly is *all*?"

"A fabulous career, gorgeous apartment, sexy boyfriend who adores you. You've got it made."

No one has it made, Sarah thought. Certainly not her. Aloud, she said, "You make it sound like my life's a fairy tale. And it isn't."

"Oh, I don't mean to imply you haven't worked very hard for everything you have. I know how dedicated you've had to be to make a go of the business. But you're a success and John's wonderful. He sends you flowers, gives you extravagant gifts. He'd never do anything as tacky as Chuck did."

Sarah started to reply, then stopped. It was true that she couldn't see John saying, "We're getting too close. Goodbye." That *was* tacky. John would never handle any situation in a way that showed a lack of class. He would be too afraid that would point to his humble roots, his lack of "breeding."

On the other hand, he never talked of commitment. And when they were apart for these long periods while he traveled on business... well, Sarah didn't ask if he spent all his free time alone. The fact that she couldn't ask him said something about their relationship.

He called often, as he always did while away. But

he didn't say, "It's lonely without you." For the first time, Sarah admitted to herself her doubts that his time away from her was spent alone.

Finally, she faced something that had lain just under the surface of her thoughts for a while now. Her relationship with John was a thoroughly contemporary one—no obligation on either side, no sacrifices asked or given. Perversely, Sarah, who liked to think of herself as a thoroughly modern young woman, and who only recently had congratulated herself on being exactly where she wanted to be, wasn't happy about this.

The waiter brought the bill, and Sarah paid, politely overriding Lara's objections.

"I should pay for lunch, at least, if not for the therapy," Lara insisted.

Sarah returned Lara's brave smile. "I'll write it off as a business lunch. And just to make sure it's almost true, we'll talk about the Bay Radio and TV account on the way back to the office."

But as they talked of work, Sarah's thoughts strayed to other things. So, Lara thought she had it made. She had thought so too, at one point. Now she had her doubts.

"HELLO, SARAH."

The voice was unmistakable. Sarah felt her entire body tense slightly as she sat in the chair behind her desk. It had been a week since they'd talked. It seemed like a year.

"Hello, Bryce, how are you?"

Her tone was cordial, slightly impersonal—exactly the opposite of what she was actually feeling.

"I'm in the city," he explained. "Something unexpected came up and I had to drive down this afternoon. Rather than turn right around and go back again, I thought I'd spend the night."

"Oh." How silly that sounded, Sarah thought, irritated at her lack of aplomb.

Bryce continued, "What I'm getting at, rather clumsily, is that I'd like to take you out to dinner. That is, if you'll excuse the last-minute invitation and if you're not busy."

I'm definitely not busy, Sarah thought. She'd actually planned a quiet evening catching up on laundry and other boring household tasks. With John away, her evenings were never busy.

"I suppose we could use this opportunity to go over the ad campaign—" she began.

But he cut her short. "Sarah, I want you to understand that this invitation has nothing to do with business. It's a plain old-fashioned date. You put on your best perfume, I find a charming restaurant, we talk about ourselves, art, politics, whatever strikes our fancy. Anything but business."

She laughed lightly. "Well, that's certainly clear enough." *So,* she thought, *it's out in the open. No more pretense about getting together for business purposes only.* It was a heady thought—and one fraught with obvious dangerous potential.

"Well..." she drew out the word thoughtfully.

"And don't prolong my agony," he added. "Say yes and tell me how soon you can be ready."

Sarah felt a rush of excitement. He wasn't going to let her out of this. And she was glad. Glancing at the clock on her desk, she saw that it was nearly 5:00 P.M. Another half hour to finish her work, fifteen minutes to get home, an hour to shower, dress, do her hair and makeup.... "Seven o'clock," she answered simply.

"See you then."

When he hung up, she cradled the receiver on her shoulder for a moment, then put it down. Her face was suffused with a glow of delicious anticipation.

THEY DROVE DOWN the Embarcadero, past the piers, Fisherman's Wharf and the factories-turned-into-shopping centers, The Cannery and Ghirardelli Square. Just before the yacht harbor, Bryce turned left toward the city.

Without looking at Sarah, he said quietly, "You look lovely."

She smiled softly. She'd rummaged through her closet for ten minutes before finally selecting a blue silk jacquard capelet blouse with full billowing sleeves, and a matching skirt patterned with zigzags of jewel-toned blues, golds and bronzy browns. A wide leather belt was sashed at the waist, and she wore dark brown lizard-skin boots.

All in all, she felt rather gypsyish, which was appropriate, since her mood was distinctly daring.

Looking at Bryce, who was impressive, as usual, in an ivory turtleneck sweater under a rust-colored tweed jacket, she asked, "Where are we going, by the way?"

"Here," he answered, pulling the car into an empty space on the street.

They were only a few yards from Union Street. As they walked down that charming street, past Victorian houses converted into boutiques and restaurants, Bryce held Sarah's hand. It felt very nice, indeed, she decided.

He paused in front of a small art gallery and scrutinized a painting in the window. It was distinctly modern, a jumble of vivid reds and blues in no discernible pattern.

"What do you think?" he asked, turning to Sarah.

She cocked her head to one side and eyed the painting carefully. Finally, she replied, "Striking. But not my cup of tea. I prefer art that makes a clear statement. Or that just plain looks nice."

He smiled. "You're old-fashioned. I suspected it. Now, I'm sure."

The corners of her full mouth tilted up in a wry smile. "And here I thought I was the quintessential woman of the eighties—ambitious, independent, on my own and happy to be that way."

The look he gave her from those shrewd greenish-brown eyes was piercing. "Are you, indeed?"

Her smile evaporated under that penetrating gaze. She'd thought she was all the things she described. Now, with this man, she was no longer entirely sure.

To change what had turned into a disturbing subject, Sarah said, "I'm starving! I thought you promised to feed me—and in someplace charming, at that."

He laughed. "I did. I think you'll find this restaurant charming." Pointing to a blue-and-white-striped awning across the street, he finished, "And it's right over there. Do you think you can keep from fainting with hunger long enough to cross the street?"

"I'll try."

A moment later they were seated at a corner table in the Forty-Niner Bar and Grill. The decor was refreshingly simple and down-to-earth—ancient sepia photographs of gold miners and mining towns and mining paraphernalia. The odors emanating from the dishes that the waiters delivered to the tables around them were delicious and intriguing.

"I think I like this place already," Sarah announced as a plate of classic English mutton chops sailed past on a tray carried by a hurrying waiter.

Bryce smiled. "I'm glad. I love it, but I'm a bit prejudiced. Friends of mine run it."

At that moment, a man about Bryce's age came

up to them. "Bryce! It's about time you stopped by. I was beginning to think you didn't like our cooking."

"You know better than that." Turning to Sarah, Bryce said, "This is Art Lauffer. Art, meet Sarah Montgomery."

"How do you do?" she asked, extending a hand.

Art, who had carrot-red hair and freckles, shook her hand energetically. "Great to meet you."

"Join us," Bryce invited.

"Just for a minute," he said, sitting down at their table. "As you can see, we're busy tonight."

Bryce explained to Sarah, "Art and his wife, Shari, run the Forty-Niner." Turning back to Art, he asked, "Is she in the kitchen?"

"Sorry, no. She's up at Stoney Creek."

"That old Victorian place you bought near Madrona?"

"Yes." To Sarah, Art explained, "We found this rather dilapidated but definitely charming old Victorian farmhouse not too far from Bryce's place. We want to turn it into an inn."

"How fun," Sarah exclaimed. "I've always had a secret desire to do that."

"I think everyone wants to do it at some time or other. We all have this fantasy of a quaint intimate little place. Unfortunately, a great deal of work has to be done to turn a filthy old house into a quaint intimate inn. Shari's spending all her free time up there, while I hold down the fort here."

"Well, I think you've got the best of both worlds," Sarah replied. "A marvelous restaurant in the city, and a lovely old inn in wine country. How did you come to open up a restaurant?"

"Both Shari and I have always enjoyed cooking. But we weren't into nouvelle cuisine. We wanted to go back to the old-fashioned concept of the grill restaurant—the open-fire tradition. We started the Forty-Niner as an informal neighborhood café."

Glancing around at the packed restaurant, Sarah commented, "You've certainly done well."

"Yes, thank goodness." Clearly curious, Art added, "By the way, what's your line of work?"

"I'm in advertising."

"Sarah's going to make my new wine famous," Bryce explained. "She's come up with a terrific name—Benedict Vintage Recherché."

"Recherché... mmm, is it as good as it sounds?" he asked Bryce teasingly.

Bryce smiled. "I hope so. Speaking of wine, may I see what you've got?"

"Sure. You know the way to the wine cellar. I'll stay here and keep your lovely friend company."

"Just remember you're a happily married man."

Art made a mock frown. "Did you have to remind me?"

When Bryce was gone, Art said, "He's one of my oldest friends, you know."

"When did you meet?" Sarah asked, unable to contain her curiosity. This was an unexpected opportunity to find out more about Bryce.

"We were freshmen at Berkeley fifteen years ago. God, it doesn't seem like it should be that long ago. Anyway, we were involved in the free-speech movement."

"Bryce?" Sarah exclaimed, surprised.

Art laughed. "I know. He seems so traditional. And he is, in many ways. But he has a sense of right and wrong that goes beyond superficial political boundaries of liberal and conservative. He's just about the most decent person I know."

Sarah was dying to ask Art about Bryce's ex-wife. Since they were such good friends, Art must have known her. But she had no idea how to broach the subject in a subtle way. Finally, she said, "I've met Adam. He's an adorable little boy."

"Yeah, he's pretty cute. The spitting image of Bryce. Though Shari always says she can see Melissa in him."

"Melissa?" Sarah asked encouragingly.

"Adam's mother." Art hesitated, unsure how much Sarah knew.

"I know Bryce is divorced," she explained. "But he hasn't said much about his ex-wife."

"He wouldn't. It was a pretty bitter divorce." His expression hardened. "I always thought Melissa was self-centered, but I didn't think she'd be *that* uncaring. I can still remember Adam crying for his mother, and she wasn't there." He shook his head soberly. "It was a shame."

At that moment, Bryce returned carrying a bottle of wine. It was a French Bordeaux and when Art saw the label, he grinned. "Traitor," he teased.

"I'm merely sampling the competition," Bryce replied with equanimity.

"Well, I've got to get back to the kitchen," Art announced, rising. "It's been a pleasure, Sarah. You know, Shari and I will have to talk to you sometime about publicizing our inn, once we get it ready to open."

"Please do that. I'd love to help you with it," Sarah responded sincerely.

When Art was gone, Bryce said warmly, "He's a good friend. Just about my oldest friend, in fact."

"He told me."

"Don't tell me he regaled you with stories about our college pranks?"

Sarah grinned. "Not in embarrassing detail."

The waiter appeared. After chatting briefly with Bryce, whom he knew, he took their order for grilled lamb shoulder with loin chops.

When the waiter had gone, Sarah said, "By the way, I forgot to ask what *you* thought of that painting we looked at.

Bryce answered, "Me? I hated it."

"Then why on earth did you ask me what I thought?"

"Just checking to see if we liked the same things. As I thought, we *do*."

Sarah was silent for a moment. She knew what Bryce was getting at—the kinship between them that she'd felt from the very beginning.

Fortunately, at that point the waiter brought their salads and Sarah was saved from having to reply to Bryce's comment.

The meal was delicious, and by the time they were lingering over coffee, Sarah felt pleasurably full and relaxed.

"Adam started going to kindergarten," Bryce told her.

"Ah... was the first day traumatic?"

Bryce smiled. "For me, not him. He waved goodbye and happily hurried into the classroom, anxious to be with the other kids. I felt abandoned."

Sarah's expression was warmly sympathetic. "I can understand that. Being able to work out of your home must have made you feel very close to him."

"It has. Now that he's gone, the house seems incredibly quiet."

Sarah reflected on the fact that her own home was very quiet. It had never bothered her before. She wondered what it would be like to live once more in a house that was alive with people, noise, action. The thought was surprisingly appealing.

When the waiter brought the bill, Bryce paid it, then asked Sarah, "Do you feel like working off some of this dinner?"

She smiled. "Sure."

They drove down to Marina Boulevard, parked, then walked over to the yacht harbor. Sarah had brought a brown wool cape, which she wore now, for the night was cold. On the water only yards away, boats bobbed up and down gently. In the distance, Sarah could make out the lights from Sausalito and Tiburon across the bay.

She leaned against the railing and looked at the boats. It was a clear night, with no mist. Bryce stood silently watching Sarah for a few minutes, then said, "A penny for your thoughts."

"Well, they're pretty prosaic thoughts, actually. I was just remembering when I first came to San Francisco. I drove down here and looked at the yachts on one side and those fabulous mansions on the other. I thought how exciting it would be to live in that rarefied atmosphere of wealth."

"And now?"

"Ah, *now* I understand that money can't buy happiness." She smiled up at Bryce. "I told you they were prosaic thoughts."

"How did you reach such a perceptive conclusion?"

"By rubbing elbows with wealthy people."

They were both silent for a moment. Then Bryce said, "I was pleasantly surprised you were free tonight. I expected you to be busy."

She knew what he was getting at. She responded matter-of-factly, "John is working in Hawaii for a few weeks. So my nights tend to be free."

"I'm glad."

Determined to change the subject, she asked, "Did you grow up rich?"

He smiled. "No. We were land poor. Grandfather was a simple man, really, who cared more about the quality of the wine he produced than the profit he made from it. My father, as I've said, provided any financial security the Benedicts had."

"If Recherché is successful, you could become rather wealthy."

"Yes. But that isn't my motivation in doing it."

"What is your motivation?"

He was thoughtful for a moment. "My father wanted to produce an excellent wine that would be available to most people. I want to do the same. Also, I want to honor his memory by seeing his dream fulfilled."

"You're so lucky," Sarah's tone was pensive. "You seem to know exactly who you are and what you want out of life."

His hazel eyes watched her carefully. "Don't you? You certainly appeared to have a handle on everything that first day I walked into your office—" he offered her a quick wry grin "—hot from firing your competitor. And clearly you're very good at what you do. Don't you know what you want out of life?"

Hunching her shoulders inside the cape, she pulled it closer around herself. The breeze off the bay was brisk. And his question was disturbing. Did she know what she wanted?

Until that day—when he brought the Recherché campaign to her, she'd been right on target with who she was and where she wanted to be.

She'd always considered herself fortunate. Her middle-class background was an unusually solid one in terms of contemporary life-styles. Her parents still loved each other, still lived in the same home they established when they married, still believed that the family unit was the cornerstone of society. As did both sets of grandparents... and numerous members of her large extended family. Her brother and sister, both married and parents, felt as she did. Lucky to be who and what they were.

From the time she'd entered college, Sarah realized that she did want more for herself than the other members of the distaff side of her family. She'd set some difficult goals, but so far had been able to achieve them.

She'd enjoyed school and had worked hard, graduating from university with honors and a job offer from a prestigious advertising firm. She'd loved living in Minneapolis, loved the life-style available to a young woman. She'd taken advantage of every opportunity to "improve her lot," so to speak.

There'd been only one bad time, she'd gotten too close to becoming seriously involved. That was when she was twenty-five. And that was when she'd done some serious thinking about what she wanted out of life.

She knew it was more than what happened to her when she kissed Kenny Olson. There was, deep inside her, a magnetic needle that kept pointing her in a certain direction...toward a special promise of fulfillment. Paying attention to that current, she'd kept moving and pushing, always up. Moving to San Francisco was moving up. John Carr was moving up. Opening her own agency was moving up. Something that only she knew about directed her, and she had heeded its guidance until now. *Until I met you, Bryce Benedict,* she admitted to herself.

Sarah wondered what he would say if she'd said all this aloud. What would he think if she dared to be honest enough to tell him that until the day he fired Grant Holcomb, she'd known what she wanted.

She looked up at him to see that he'd moved even closer to her. "I thought I did." The words were whispered, hesitant. His nearness did something strange to her senses. She felt her blood race and her heart pound. Her breathing had grown erratic. He was so near she could see the dark pupils of his eyes narrowed now in desire.

"Sarah." The word was as intimate as any caress.

"Don't," she began, but it was too late. Her word was spoken against his mouth. His lips were pressing against hers, his arms were holding her captive. Their bodies touched—leg against leg, hard chest against soft pliant breasts. The kiss was sweeter than honey, more intoxicating than wine.

Sarah was lost in a private world of heady sensations. Her body tingled ecstatically with wanting. All of her wanted all of him, not just this kiss. Even though she felt the strength of his arms clasping her to him, she felt suspended in a rich warmth of passion. Her heart was filled with a feeling she'd never known before. It was at once frightening and reassuring.

When he finally let her go, she took a deep breath of the cool, salty air and tried to steady her reeling senses.

"It seems that every time we're together, I end up being kissed," she said with a forced attempt at lightness.

He smiled tenderly. "Then you should be prepared for it, by now."

Ah, but I'll never be prepared for the way you make me feel, Sarah thought.

Aloud, she said, "I think I'd better go home."

To her relief, he didn't argue. He took her back to his car. To make conversation on the drive toward Telegraph Hill, Sarah asked, "Where are you staying?"

"At the Fairmont."

Of course, she thought. That venerable old hotel would be his style.

At her door, he started to speak. But she stopped him. "No... please. I'm rather tired and I think I'd just like to go to bed."

He smiled in understanding. "I won't make the obvious reply to that intriguing statement."

"It was a lovely evening, Bryce."

"I thought so too. Good night, Sarah." He kissed her forehead lightly, then turned and walked away.

Later, as she lay in bed, Sarah felt a deep dissatisfaction, a yearning. She knew perfectly well what she yearned for. Only minutes away, Bryce, too, was probably lying in bed. Perhaps thinking of her.

The thought brought a warm flush to her cheeks and a tingling sensation deep within her.

7

LATE THURSDAY AFTERNOON Sarah was sitting at her desk working intently.

"Hey, boss."

She looked up to see Richard standing in the open doorway. Putting down her pen, she sighed tiredly and said, "If it's a problem, file it under *p*. I don't have time for it."

"You're working too hard."

"Tell me about it."

"What you need is some good wholesome food— Chinese style."

Sarah smiled. "Is that an invitation to your parents' restaurant?"

"It is. My venerable grandmother's celebrating her seventy-fifth birthday and my entire extended family of aunts, uncles, cousins, etcetera, are coming to the shindig. I thought you and Lara might like to join Ginger and me."

"Oh, Richard, that sounds marvelous. It's sweet of you to include Lara."

"Well, I know she's been having a rough time lately. A real Cantonese feast should cheer up. Anyway, it's tomorrow night at eight."

"Great!"

The next evening Sarah sat at a small table in the banquet room of On Lock Sam's restaurant. With her were Richard, Lara and Ginger, an exquisitely beautiful Chinese girl. Since getting to know Richard, Sarah had often eaten at his parents' restaurant.

The food was delicious, Richard's parents were
warm and friendly. What she liked most about this
place and these people was the sense of continuity
that pervaded their lives. Richard's people had first
come to California in the late 1800's, part of the
coolie labor force that built the railroads. At the turn
of the century, they had opened this restaurant,
rebuilt it after the great earthquake of 1906, and
passed the ownership down from father to son.

Sarah knew Richard's parents were disappointed
that their only son had chosen a different career. In
that sense, she and Richard shared something in
common, besides a mutual respect and liking. He too
had left a sheltered upbringing to make a different
kind of life for himself. He was happy with his decision, especially after coming to work for Sarah. But
he still, like Sarah, remained close to his tight-knit
family. When he first asked Sarah to meet them, she
was very touched. She knew what they meant to
him.

As she sat in the banquet room, she enjoyed the
most delicious dinner of Chinese food she'd ever
tasted.

"Richard, I love this fish-ball-and-bean-curd cas-
serole," she said to him. "Can I get the recipe?"

He put a finger to his lips. "Sh. Don't ask too
loudly. I'll wait for an opportune time, then ask my
mother. For you, she may consider revealing the old
family secret."

Ginger laughed, her dark eyes sparkling merrily.
"Old family secret? I'll have you know, Sarah, that
Richard's mother got this particular recipe from *me*.
And I'll be happy to pass it along."

Richard grimaced in mock anger. "Woman, you've
just ruined the whole effect—Oriental inscrutability,
secret family recipes, etc."

Lara interjected happily, "Well, I for one am just

plain happy to be here, enjoying this wonderful food, secret recipe or no secret recipe. And I want to thank you for inviting me. I know you're trying to keep my spirits up."

"Is it working?" Richard asked with a frank smile.

Lara met his smile. "Yes."

As Sarah listened to the friendly banter, she looked at Richard and Ginger. They made a perfect couple—both darkly attractive, short and slim.

Richard excused himself to take his gift to his grandmother. Lara left to refill her plate from the lavish buffet, and Sarah and Ginger were alone at the small table.

"How's your job going?" Sarah asked. Ginger was a buyer for a popular boutique, and Sarah enjoyed hearing her discuss the latest trends in fashion.

"Hectic, as usual," Ginger answered, tossing her long black hair behind her shoulders. "Customers have started buying for the fall and winter seasons and we're having to make last-minute adjustments according to what's selling and what isn't. Fortunately, Richard's too busy himself to complain about not seeing much of me."

"I really depend on him a lot," Sarah said. "Did he tell you that I talked to him about a promotion?"

Ginger grinned. "He couldn't wait to tell me, Sarah, he's so excited. And I'm so relieved. For a while, I thought he was just going to float through life, not caring much how his career was going."

"He's too talented not to be a big success."

"Oh, I know he's talented. But until now, he's never been ambitious. And that was a problem, because I am. Going to work for you was the best thing that could have happened to his career."

Looking at Ginger, listening to her, Sarah thought

how similar her relationship with Richard was to Sarah's relationship with John. In both cases, career success seemed to be of paramount importance. It was definitely a change, Sarah thought, from the time when men were the sole breadwinners and women were the housewives.

Whether or not that was entirely a change for the better was debatable, Sarah decided.

Just then, Richard returned. While he and Ginger talked, Sarah glanced around. The decor was as delightful as the food. The Wongs had spent generations accumulating a treasury of antique Chinese art for exhibit in the restaurant. Porcelains, bronzes, paintings, ancient weapons and a magnificent collection of Chinese god figurines adorned the large room.

Sarah gazed in fascination at one particular wooden figure presiding in serenity against the back wall.

"That's Kuan Yin," Richard told her. "Goddess of Mercy."

"I could use a little of that," Lara quipped, sitting down at the table.

Everyone laughed, glad that Lara was able to joke about her lost love.

"Richard," Sarah asked, "in all the times I've been here, I've never thought to ask you. What does On Lock Sam mean?"

"Contented heart. Kind of pretty, isn't it?"

"Yes. Very pretty."

But as Sarah sat back in her chair and listened to the first of many toasts that would be made to Richard's venerable grandmother, she couldn't concentrate on the party. Instead, she found herself musing pensively on the fact that her own heart was far from contented. A month ago, she would have said it was. But now, after meeting Bryce, she felt caught up in a whirling vortex of discontent that made her question herself in a way she hadn't done since deciding to leave Minneapolis years earlier.

Bryce. He came into her thoughts no matter where she was, what she was doing. Did he think of her the way she often thought of him?

BRYCE AND THADDEUS SAT on the deck, enjoying the mild summer evening. The sun had set many hours ago, and a large candle set inside a clear hurricane lamp provided a soft light.

"Looks like a good year," Thaddeus said.

Bryce smiled affectionately at the older man. "You always say that."

"And I'm always right," Thaddeus responded. After a moment, he continued, "By the way, will Sarah Montgomery be coming back soon?"

Startled, Bryce asked a little too quickly, "Why do you ask?"

"Oh, no reason." Thaddeus's tone was carefully casual. "Adam asked about her today. He was rather taken with her. She is a very nice young lady. And pretty too."

"Thaddeus..." Bryce began warningly.

"Now, Bryce, I'm merely pointing out the obvious. Sarah Montgomery is a nice, attractive young lady. I must say, you seem touchy on the subject."

"I'm not touchy. But I know what you're getting at."

"It's been three years since a woman lived in this house. That's too long for a healthy young man like yourself to be alone."

Bryce smiled dryly. "I've hardly been a monk. You know that."

"I'm not talking about filling a physical need. Heaven knows there have been plenty of attractive young women willing to do that for you. I'm talking about someone you can build a life with."

"Thaddeus, I hardly know Sarah well enough to consider building a life with her. And besides," he added irritably, "I don't think she's looking for a chance to become a housewife. She's very definitely a career woman."

"And does that mean she couldn't be a wife and mother, as well?"

"She may not want to take on the responsibility of raising someone else's child," Bryce pointed out.

"Nonsense. She got along extremely well with Adam. He liked her. And he doesn't like most of the women you go out with."

"Whether or not she gets along well with Adam is beside the point. I told you—she's got a high-powered career that she's obviously dedicated to."

"Bryce, just because Melissa's career came between you two doesn't mean—"

"Thaddeus!" Bryce's tone was curt.

Thaddeus sighed heavily. "Very well. Enough said."

Suddenly Bryce felt a pang of guilt. He'd talked to Thaddeus just then as a master to a servant, which was not how he viewed their relationship. He began hesitantly, "I'm sorry...."

"No, it's okay. Really. I'll stop trying to play Cupid."

Bryce grinned. "All right. And I'll stop biting your head off."

Thaddeus took a final sip of the wine he'd been drinking. Then he rose. "Well, it's getting very late. I'll be off to bed. Good night, Bryce."

As he turned to go, Bryce asked tentatively, "So you like her?"

"I do, indeed. There's something very fine about her."

"And Adam likes her?"

"Yes."

For a moment Bryce was silent. Then he finished, "Good night, Thaddeus."

In a moment, Thaddeus was gone, and Bryce sat alone with the sound of the wind rustling through the trees and night birds calling hauntingly.

Sarah...there *was* something very fine about her. And despite Bryce's insistence that he hardly knew her, the fact was he already liked her a great deal. He hadn't felt this way about any of the women he'd dated since his divorce. As Thaddeus so bluntly, and accurately, put it, they filled a need. But nothing more.

But Sarah...when he kissed her it was as if his heart came alive again after being in a state of limbo for a long, long time. He wanted her as he had never wanted a woman since the early days with Melissa.

But it was all wrong, a voice inside him pointed out. She doesn't want what you have to offer. She wants the life she has. And the man she has.

Bryce felt a rush of jealousy as he remembered John Carr. Too handsome, too glib, he told himself. But he recognized that such a man was immensely appealing to women.

"Hell!" Bryce muttered under his breath. He felt a tumultuous mixture of emotions—anger, jealousy, desire. But at the heart of it all was simple need—he needed to see Sarah again. But he had no idea when that would happen. They were both incredibly busy at the moment.

Then he realized that while he couldn't see her right now, he could talk to her. He went into his study, but hesitated as he picked up the phone. It was very late and she might already be asleep. Finally deciding to chance it, he dialed her number.

"Hello?"

"Sarah, it's Bryce."

There was a pause, and even through the telephone he could sense her pleasant surprise.

"Is there a problem?" she asked.

"No. I just wanted to talk to you. Is this a bad time?"

"No. I was just reading and drinking a glass of your Recherché. I was out earlier and wanted to unwind before I went to bed."

"Sounds wonderful. What are you reading?"

"A book of poetry—Elizabeth Barrett Browning's *Sonnets from the Portuguese*."

"Now *that* sounds interesting. Why don't you read one to me?"

"Bryce." Her tone was reproving.

"I'm serious. Actually, I like poetry. Pick out one."

"I don't think—"

"Please." His tone was cajoling, as irresistible as he could possibly be.

She relented. "All right. Let's see...."

He heard her rustling through the pages of the book. "Here's a nice one." She read softly.

Unless you can muse in a crowd all day,
    On the absent face that fixed you;
Unless you can love, as the angels may,
    With the breadth of heaven betwixt you;
Unless you can dream that his faith is fast,
    Through behoving and unbehoving;
Unless you can *die* when the dream is past—
    Oh never call it loving!

When she finished, there was a pregnant pause. Then Bryce asked in a husky voice, "Do you muse about me when we're apart?"

There was a catch in her voice as she countered, "I don't think I should answer that."

He laughed softly. "That's an answer, in a way, isn't it?" Before she could argue, he finished in an intimate tone, "Good night, Sarah. Pleasant dreams."

HE BEGAN TO CALL her often. As Sarah sat in her apartment at night, she found herself half-waiting for his call, rushing to answer the phone when it rang. Their conversations were wide-ranging. She talked about her work, he talked about his. They discussed the weather, politics, Adam. Every time Bryce tried to steer the conversation to anything more intimate, Sarah carefully changed the subject or bade him goodnight. She enjoyed hearing from him too much to ask him not to call. But she had no intention of getting any more involved with him than she already was.

Then one evening when Sarah had been expecting Bryce's call for hours, the phone finally rang.

Her voice was breathless when she said, "Hello."

"Sarah! How is my lady tonight?"

It was John, not Bryce. To her chagrin, Sarah felt disappointment rather than pleasure. Recovering her poise, she responded, "Fine. How are you?"

"Keeping busy. This whole project has turned into such a mess, I don't know when I'll be home."

"Oh, I'm sorry to hear that." It was a lie. She wasn't really sorry. The thought of John's eventual return didn't bring a surge of anticipation; if anything, Sarah was relieved at his continued absence. It meant she could put off dealing with the questions she'd begun to have about their relationship.

"You sound tired. I hope I didn't wake you."

"No, I haven't gone to bed yet." *My lonely bed,* Sarah thought. Was John's bed lonely too, she wondered.

As if in answer to her unspoken question, John

said, "I miss you. I wish we could be together to-night."

Something in his voice caught at her heart. That old charm worked like magic on her senses.

"I miss you too," she replied, and at that moment, she meant it.

They talked for a long time, John explaining all the problems he was having with the project. He was obviously feeling down, and Sarah knew that was why he had called her. She felt at once pleased and resentful.

When she finally hung up, it was nearly eleven. She felt utterly exhausted. It had been a very long day, and the call from John hadn't helped. It played havoc with her emotions, making her feel very confused.

She needed a good night's sleep, Sarah told herself. Taking off her pink silk robe, she got into bed. Just as she was reaching over to turn out the lamp on her bedside table, the telephone rang again.

"Sarah."

It was Bryce.

Before she could respond, he said hesitantly, "I'm sorry to call so late. I tried earlier but your line was busy."

"Yes...." The word trailed off helplessly. She had no idea what to say.

With amazing perception, Bryce said gently, "I take it you were talking to John Carr."

"Yes."

There was a horribly awkward pause. "Well, you sound sleepy. And it's late. I'd better let you go."

"No, please, Bryce." Suddenly she wanted to talk to him, to hear his voice. It didn't matter what he said. "I'm not a bit tired. What have you been up to? How's Adam?"

He hesitated. "Well...Adam's fine." A note of

amusement crept into his voice. "He made a chocolate sandwich today."

"A chocolate sandwich?"

"Yes—chocolate sauce poured between two slices of bread. Can you believe it? Thaddeus said it's the beginning of a very creative chef."

Sarah laughed softly.

He continued, "What are you doing?"

"Just getting ready to go to sleep."

"Me too. This is a pleasant time of night. The house is quiet. Adam's asleep. When I looked in on him a few minutes ago, he looked...." He paused.

"Angelic," finished Sarah.

"That's the word. I like this time. It's peaceful."

"I know. I like it too. Even in the city it's rather quiet now."

"Sarah... I'm coming into San Francisco this weekend."

She didn't say anything, but she held her breath expectantly.

"Can I see you Saturday?"

She should refuse, she knew. Only minutes earlier she'd told John she missed him. And now.... She didn't have the heart to fight what she felt. "Yes. What time?"

"Noon. I'd like to spend the day with you. How do you feel about the exotic Orient?"

Sarah laughed. "Are we going to explore Chinatown?"

"No. How do you feel about a picnic in the park and—"

"Ah," she broke in, "exotic Orient indeed. A visit to the Japanese Tea Garden." How nice, she told herself. "That sounds marvelous."

"I'll see you then. Good night, Sarah."

"Good night," she whispered.

8

BRYCE ARRIVED PROMPTLY AT NOON and shortly afterward they were driving along John F. Kennedy Drive in Golden Gate Park. As they neared the Botanical Gardens, Bryce asked if she'd like a stroll before lunch.

"Did Thaddeus prepare a feast?" Sarah asked, already enjoying the day.

"He told me to wish you *bon appetit*," he replied, grinning at her. "I did my part. I brought a bottle of Benedict Vintage Recherché."

Leaving the car, they began walking toward the Conservatory of Flowers. Ahead of them, a large wedding party was congregating on the sidewalk and flight of concrete steps leading up to the main entrance. When they reached the stairs, Bryce and Sarah stepped aside so that the photographer could finish the picture-taking. Several small children kept breaking rank and had to be rearranged into the proper alignment.

The entire bridal party was Japanese. While they were all in western dress, there was not one word of English spoken. The bride, lovely in white satin with a swirl of tulle floating behind her, looked very serious until the groom whispered in her ear. Then she giggled and when the photographer ducked behind the camera, she was smiling radiantly.

As they observed this happy tableau, Sarah thought what an appropriate place it was to take wedding pictures. Every time she saw this building, she was reminded of a wedding cake. She supposed it was because the Conservatory, all wood and glass with ornate cupolas atop its domes, was painted white. In the midday sunlight, it appeared gossamerlike and glistened with mother-of-pearl fragility.

As the wedding party dispersed, Sarah and Bryce were free to make their way up the steps. "That was very pleasant, wasn't it?" she asked. "A bit public, but a wonderful background for wedding pictures."

"How come a beautiful girl like you is not married?" Bryce asked, without apologizing for being too personal.

Sarah gave a quick glance to see if he was serious or teasing. She saw his eyebrows lift in mock astonishment and heard him chuckle. "I'd really like to know. I just couldn't think of a better way to inquire."

"I've just not been ready to make the kind of commitment that I think marriage demands. I love my work, I'm happy with where I am in my life." She smiled at him to soften the words and stopped short of saying that the man she was involved with was not the marrying kind.

The time passed quickly and when they had finished touring the greenhouse and gardens and were again making their way to the street, Sarah turned once more to enjoy the sight. "It looks as if it were made of spun sugar, doesn't it?" The lawns were bright green and the flower beds colorful with September blooms. She thought again of the bride and groom and spoke aloud, "A beautiful place on a beautiful day. I hope this kind of sunshine stays in the bridal couple's life. They've had a good beginning."

Bryce gave her a long thoughtful look and Sarah wondered why she'd been so taken with the wedding party.

Back in the car, Bryce continued driving through the park until they found a pleasant place to eat their lunch. They sat on a red-checked blanket spread on the grass and ate flaky croissants, thinly sliced ham, sharp cheddar cheese and fresh fruit. The Recherché was chilled and delicious.

From the Music Concourse nearby came the mellow sounds of woodwinds—clarinets and a flute, a vibraharp and a bass. Backing up the ensemble was a rhythm section of bongos and congo drums. The mood and texture of the music was calm. Almost melancholy, Sarah reflected. "That's lovely music, isn't it? But plaintive."

Bryce smiled at Sarah. "Not plaintive. Exotic. Mysterious. Rare—recherché, like you." He leaned back against the tree trunk and bit into a pear.

"Would you like a rundown on the progress of the ad campaign?" she asked, thinking to change the subject.

"No," he replied, still smiling at her. "I'd rather talk about you."

"The campaign is much more interesting. Let me tell you about it." She was smiling, but her tone was determined. Briefly she told him about the radio stations where commercials would be running, and named the magazines and newspapers where the print ads would appear. "I think Grant Holcomb was right in selecting the biggest newspapers in ten target cities," she said, "so I've gone along with that strategy."

"We are staying with west of the Rockies for the newspapers, aren't we? For this first foray?"

"You're the boss. I don't know that I agree, but since that was your considered opinion, I followed your wishes." She saluted him with her glass, and with a teasing grin added, "Heaven knows I don't want to meet Grant's fate."

Bryce nodded approvingly and told her that was wise.

"By the end of the first week of the campaign, there should be very few wine lovers who haven't heard of Recherché," Sarah finished.

"Well, your campaign is certainly enough to pique their interest. They'll try it, at least. I only hope they like it."

"They'll love it," Sarah responded confidently as she swirled the wine in the goblet and sniffed its fruity bouquet.

Bryce laughed, then asked, "Are you always so partial to the products you sell?"

"Only the ones that I think are excellent. Is there anything else you'd like to know?"

"There's a lot—but not about the campaign." His gaze was direct. Sarah tried to meet it without flinching, but she felt a flush creep up her cheeks. "I really like your understated style. There's an elegance about—"

"I believe" she interrupted, "in the theory of quality rather than quantity. Sometimes less is more. A hint...a glance...a whisper, if you will, is quite provocative. You've heard the statement, if you want to get someone's attention, whisper."

She'd hoped to get this conversation back to business, but she could tell by the way he was looking at her that he was determined to pursue a more personal tack. *Every time I'm with this man for more than ten minutes,* she thought, *I feel that if I make one false move, I'll be in peril.*

As she continued to look into his eyes, forcing herself to meet that deliberate assessment, she watched his gaze soften and she wondered why she had used the word peril. Peril meant serious risk. Then she heard him say, "For someone as beautiful as you are, it would work. If you whisper, you'll get my attention. If I whisper, will I get yours?" His voice was low and husky. It was an incredibly intimate moment as they continued to look at each other and thought of all the private things they'd like to know about each other.

Suddenly the mood was broken by a bright red ball that came bouncing onto their blanket. Bryce grabbed it just as it was about to knock over the bottle of wine. Twin boys, no more than five years old, ran up to them, then stopped, with shy expressions on their faces.

Grinning, Bryce tossed the ball to the closest boy, who caught it awkwardly. Then, laughing, the two ran off a little way and began tossing it back and forth to each other.

They were an adorable pair. Two thatches of straw-colored hair, two freckled faces, two sets of china-doll blue eyes, two chubby little bodies garbed in faded jeans and red-and-white-striped T-shirts. "They make a marvelous picture, don't they?" Sarah asked, turning to look once more at Bryce.

He was watching them too. "Mmm," he murmured in agreement. "They look so happy. I'll bet they're especially close because they're twins." His expression sobered as he continued, "They're not lonely, at any rate. I wish Adam wasn't."

"Adam may not have a brother or sister, but he does have you and Thaddeus. He's a very loved child. That's what matters. And," she added, hoping to bring back his smile, "he does have Rex and Pancho."

"What you say is true," Bryce responded, ignoring her humor. "I've tried to be everything to him, and Thaddeus is great, but there's a terrible void in Adam's life."

He was referring to Adam's lack of mothering. That was a very sensitive subject and she wasn't sure how to approach it. Finally, after a protracted silence, she said, "Life's hard. That sounds like a cliché, but it's true. My grandfather taught me that one must learn to deal with adversity. Overcome it—rather than be overcome by it."

"Adam's a little young to be learning such a harsh lesson."

"Yes. But it's one we all have to learn." Glancing at the merrily romping twins, she said, "No one could wish problems on a five-year-old. But an easy life isn't always possible. Adam's a strong little boy. You must believe that he'll grow up to be a strong man."

"How did you come to be so wise, Sarah Montgomery?" There was undisguised admiration in Bryce's eyes as he spoke.

Her heartbeat did a funny little number and she realized a gentling had come over her countenance. She'd seen such an expression on her mother's face too many times not to know that it was now reflected in her eyes and the soft set of her mouth. "I'm not wise," she insisted, hearing the incongruity of words and tone.

"Yes, you are. You're wise and creative and lovely and...." He paused, and she waited curiously for him to continue. Leaning forward, he finished, "You have a crumb on your cheek."

With one finger he brushed it away. She started to smile at him, but her smile dissolved as his finger continued its light stroke along the curve of her cheek and the line of her jaw. It traveled down until, with that weightless but electric touch, he tilted her chin so that his changing hazel eyes gazed directly into her own. She knew that their brownness was now glowing with what she was feeling. It had to be so.

"Sarah," he whispered.

It was all she could do to keep from lifting her lips to his, they were so close.

Everything around them—the laughing little boys, the music in the background, all sight and sound— disappeared as they focused on each other. It was a moment of intense awareness, of a connection that was invisible but terribly real.

Somewhere in the dim recesses of her mind, Sarah recognized that she'd never before felt anything like this. And yet they weren't making love, they weren't even kissing. The only physical contact was his fingertip held ever so lightly under her chin, tilting her face to meet his.

The fragile magic was shattered as the red ball came bounding back onto their blanket. Sarah caught a flash of red as it rolled past. This time, Bryce was not quick enough and the ball toppled the Recherché. Laughing, Sarah sprang to her feet to escape the froth of wine as it bubbled out of the overturned bottle.

When the ball had been returned to the boys, they gathered up their picnic things and put them in the trunk of the car. Then, hand in hand, they headed in the direction of the Japanese Tea Garden.

As they walked toward the Tea House, Sarah thanked Bryce for this trip to the exotic Orient. "This is one of my very favorite places. I often come here. I love it when the cherry blossoms are in bloom, and in the fall when the foliage is orange and golden. Today is nice too. The garden is lovely."

"Today, the garden is beautiful." There was no mistaking what he meant.

Their stroll along the path led them beside still waters, over the irregularities of stepping stones, across the trestle bridge. They stood before "The Buddha that sits through the sunny and rainy weather without a shelter." It was very large, over ten feet. "That Buddha weighs a ton and a half," Bryce mused aloud. "I know because I was so impressed when I first read about it. I made a special trip to see it. He paused, then continued in a thoughtful tone, "Funny, isn't it, what bits of trivia we store in our heads." As they turned to walk down the hill to the Tea House, he continued, "For instance, you said earlier that you came here often. Do you come alone?"

Surprised, Sarah turned to look at him. "Of course. I like to be alone sometimes. Don't you?"

"I've been alone a lot. Too much, I'm beginning to think."

Seated in the Tea House, they were served tea by a charming Japanese girl dressed in a colorful kimono. Bryce excused himself and in just a few minutes returned with a sack of fortune cookies from the gift shop. "Have a fortune," he said, offering a cookie to Sarah and taking one for himself.

"You first," she said, after she had broken the cookie and read the pink slip of paper. "What does your fortune promise?"

"It doesn't promise a thing. 'Idleness is the holiday of fools,'" he read. "Idleness is one thing I'm not guilty of." He sounded outraged.

Sarah laughed and suggested he try again.

"Is that fair? I don't have to accept what fate deals me?"

Picking up a cookie, she held it out to him. "Try again. Surely everyone should have a second chance at good fortune."

Quickly Bryce covered her hand with his. He held it for a moment, then took the cookie from her fingers and snapped it open. "If I don't like this, can I go for a third try?"

"Why not? They're your cookies," she said, laughing at him.

He looked at it, shrugged, and read: " 'You have a strong desire for a home and your family comes first.' "

"That's close to the truth, don't you think? Are you satisfied with that one?" Sarah teased, "Do you want to try again?"

"Nope, I'll keep this one. What does yours say?" He looked expectantly at her, and when she did not share it, reached across the table and took it from her. " 'You have a friendly heart and are well admired,' " he read.

Determined to keep the mood light and fun, Sarah reached for a second fortune cookie for herself. Before she could take one, he captured her hand again. "You do have a friendly heart, don't you, pretty Sarah? And you are most certainly well admired. Now that we've had the word straight from the baker, what do you see in the tea leaves?"

Sarah gazed down at the leaves lying haphazardly at the bottom of her white porcelain cup. *I wonder,* she thought, *I wonder what my future... and my fortune will be. An awful lot about my life has changed since meeting this man. I wonder if he thinks that his life has changed since meeting me.*

"A penny... or should I say a yen?" Bryce teased.

"I was thinking," she said, "about what an excellent idea you had—this trip. It's been a fun day."

"And not over yet. Are you ready to walk some more?" he asked.

She smiled. "Yes."

They went to the de Young Museum and the aquarium. Then, late in the afternoon, Bryce dropped off Sarah at her apartment, while he went on to his hotel to change for dinner.

SEVERAL HOURS LATER Sarah answered the door at her apartment. She had changed into a romantic knee-length dress of damask and lace. Her hair was in a sleek chignon.

Bryce's eyes widened in pleased approval as he took in the pale bone-linen damask paneled in antique blue with lace edging. "Now, *that* I like," he said, smiling.

Sarah felt a rush of pleasure. This was one of her favorite dresses, for it made her feel totally feminine and lovely. Giving a mock curtsy, she replied, "Why, thank you, sir."

As Bryce helped her slip into a blue-velvet coat, she was conscious of his nearness. His breath warm on the back of her neck, his hand on her shoulders—all this combined to make her feel almost giddy.

Steady, she told herself. But her fingers trembled as she picked up her evening bag.

Forcing her voice to sound normal, she asked, "Where are we going?"

"On a long journey, across the water, to a land far, far away."

At her quizzical look, Bryce laughed and explained, "We're taking the ferry to Sausalito."

She smiled. "Mmm, I love the ferry. Especially at night."

A few minutes later they were standing at the stern of the ferry as it pulled away from the pier. The lights of the city quickly receded. Sarah felt the sting of sea air on her cheeks. It was a crisp clear night, the water of the bay black and the sky dotted with twinkling stars. Bryce put his arm around her shoulders as if it was the most natural thing in the world to do. After a moment's hesitation, Sarah leaned her cheek against his chest. His tweed coat felt rough, yet pleasant.

"I'm glad to see you're not the type to get seasick," he teased.

"On a twenty-minute ferry ride?" Sarah shot back, looking up at him. "Certainly not. Remember you're talking to a girl from the land of sky-blue waters...I love to sail and paddle a canoe."

"You look so glamorous tonight, it's hard to believe you've ever done anything so sporting."

She laughed but was immensely pleased at the compliment. She wanted to look wonderful for him.

Once more she leaned her cheek against Bryce's shoulder. Feeling so comfortable in this casual embrace, Sarah wished the trip would never end. It was almost as if they were heading on a magical journey to a place out of time.

But all too soon they had docked and were in the bright lights and noisy crowds of Sausalito, a charming little village of boutiques and restaurants.

Bryce had reservations at the Seven Seas. They sat at a secluded table, ate rare steak and succulent shrimp, and talked. Sarah marveled at the easy way their conversation flowed from one topic to another. They were never at a loss; and while they didn't always agree, their differences were stimulating rather than irritating.

It seemed as if only minutes had passed instead of hours, when Bryce glanced at his watch and said, "We've got to go. The last ferry leaves shortly."

It was too cold now to remain outside. They found seats near a window inside the boat and watched as Sausalito receded behind them.

There were very few people on the ferry, and no one was sitting near them. Sarah almost felt alone with Bryce. It was a very nice feeling.

But as the ferry came closer to the city, she realized this lovely day was coming to a close—at least the social part of it. What now, she wondered. When they were back in the car, would she yawn and say *That was marvelous, but I'm rather tired now?*

And when he took her home, would he leave her at her door with a smile and a friendly good-night?

No. That, she was sure, wasn't what he planned. Nor was it what she herself wanted. She didn't want this evening to end yet.

Later, at her door, Sarah said awkwardly, "I...I had a wonderful time." When he said nothing, but continued to look at her, she asked, "Would you like to come in for coffee?"

His mouth softened in a slow seductive smile and his eyes glinted with barely suppressed desire. "I'd like to come in. But I won't pretend it's for coffee. Sarah...."

"Bryce, I—"

"I know what you're going to say. You're involved with someone else. And even if he isn't around at the moment, you don't want to be disloyal."

"Yes." The word was whispered, desolate.

"Do you love John Carr, Sarah?"

She hesitated. If she'd been asked that question a month ago, two weeks ago, she'd have said readily, "Of course." Now....

"I've been involved with John for a long time," she explained slowly. "We have a good relationship." She leaned against her door and looked away, not meeting Bryce's intent gaze. "We're good for each other, right for each other. We want the same things out of life."

"Do you?"

Sarah found it maddening that Bryce should question her statement. Of course, it was true. John *was* right for her. "We're both very into our careers."

"And that's what you want—a career?"

"Yes!" Suddenly, for no reason, she was angry with this man who made her question her feelings. "Maybe you can't understand that. Maybe you think a woman's place is in the home."

"Not exactly. But I do believe in commitment in a relationship. I know you don't have that in your relationship with him."

"How can you be so sure of that?" she asked, her brown eyes flashing furiously.

"Because you wouldn't go out with me if you did. You wouldn't let me put my arms around you ... kiss you."

Suddenly his lips were on hers and she was melting in his arms. The anger drained from her, to be replaced by a desire that was ... oh, so sweet. Involuntarily, her hands went to his chest as his arms drew her against him.

Even after she pulled back, her head was spinning and her heart pounding wildly. Looking up at Bryce through anguished eyes, she whispered, "No. This isn't right. I can't see you like this again."

Grabbing her key from her purse with shaking hands, she unlocked the door. But as she went inside, he followed, closing the door firmly behind him. He stood still as she removed her coat and hung it in the closet, refusing to look at him.

Taking her shoulders in his hands, he forced her to face him. "Sarah!"

"No. Please Bryce, don't call me at home again. I'll talk to you in the office, but that's all."

But he wasn't about to be dismissed. Things had gone too far for that. "You can't pretend any longer there's nothing between us!" As she tried to turn away, he demanded angrily, "Sarah, look at me!"

"No," she insisted, but the word was hardly out of her mouth before his lips were on hers, silencing her protest. She struggled fiercely for a split second, then suddenly her being yielded to him. Like a puppet whose strings have gone slack, she fell against him. His strong arms kept her from falling as he kissed her with an urgency that was the other side of the tenderness he'd shown her earlier. Growing bolder moment by moment, he let his lips and fingers trail down her face, her neck, her shoulders, where he pushed aside the bodice of her dress to expose the curve of her shoulder.

His rampant burning kisses intoxicated her and left her senses reeling. Before she knew what had happened, he scooped her up in his arms and carried her to the sofa. There he gently laid her down and bent to kiss her again.

Into Sarah's mind came the simple thought that she wanted to make love with this man. She wanted to give herself completely to him, to feel him be part of her.

Then her thoughts were obliterated as his kisses deepened and his hands began to caress her body through the fabric of her dress. She felt him tremble with the depth of his desire for her, and knew that she too was trembling under his touch.

She wasn't content merely to respond. Instead, she began to explore him, twining her fingers in his soft silky brown hair, running her hands down the side of his hard body.

She felt his tongue teasing its way into her mouth and she didn't resist. He probed, delved, with infinite gentleness. A flush of heat suffused her entire body and she shuddered.

Then, obviously eager to continue his exploration, his lips moved to kiss the corners of her mouth, moving to the tender spot beneath her earlobe, down her silken throat to the hollow between shoulder and neck. Impatiently, he unbuttoned her bodice enough to push the dress off her shoulder completely. As his lips grazed the tops of her quivering breasts, she felt herself arch up to press against him.

Finally, he lifted his head and stared into her eyes.

In a voice hoarse with passion, he said, "I want you, Sarah. All of you."

Then he waited, leaving the decision up to her.

I want you too, she thought with desperation. *Oh, how I want you.*

But at the same time, she knew she couldn't give herself to him on this night—not while she was still tied to another man. It would be wrong. Wrong for her, wrong for Bryce, even wrong for John, though he'd never asked for her fidelity.

She whispered in a barely audible voice, as if the words were torn from her, "I can't. Not now."

For a moment, he looked stricken. She wondered if he would understand her protest—if he retained enough self-control at this point to do so.

After what seemed an eternity, he nodded. Without saying a word, he rose and strode across the room. The door slammed shut behind him.

9

At the end of September Sarah returned to Madrona one afternoon with the final plans for the ad campaign. Summer's warmth had cooled to the chill of early fall as her car wound through the valley where grapes hung heavy on the vines. There was a sense of expectancy, of change, in the crisp air. And not just because of the changing of the seasons or the coming harvest. Within herself, Sarah felt a vague stirring that had nothing to do with the weather.

Bryce hadn't called her at home. They'd only spoken twice, and both times the conversation was solely about business. Yet Sarah hadn't stopped thinking about him, and was sure he hadn't stopped thinking about her.

John called often, but he couldn't take her mind off Bryce.

This time as Sarah pulled into the driveway of Madrona, Adam greeted her warmly as a long-lost friend. Even the dogs seemed to remember her. Pancho bounded up to her, tail wagging, yelping happily. The rather intimidating Rex was almost friendly and licked her hand when she extended it, open palmed, toward him.

Bryce was down at the winery, it seemed. So Adam played little lord of the manor and escorted Sarah into the living room. He sat talking to her until his father returned a few minutes later.

Again, as she looked at Bryce, Sarah felt that jolt of intense attraction. It never seemed to wane. Each time she saw him, it was as if she was seeing him for the first time. There was no disappointment, no lessening of the feeling she had for him. It was disconcerting, to say the least.

"Sorry I've kept you waiting," he began.

"It's all right." Smiling down at Adam, she finished, "Your son's a wonderful host."

Adam beamed happily.

"This time of year, things get pretty busy," Bryce explained.

"I knew you'd be busy. That's why I thought it would be easier if I brought everything here for you to go over before we finalize the campaign."

That was actually only half-true. The truth was that she loved coming to Madrona, loved seeing Bryce and Adam.

As if reading her mind, Bryce said, "Well, at least we can make this a mini vacation for you. Stay for dinner?"

She knew she should refuse. The last time she spent the evening with this man, he had nearly made love to her. And the memory of those golden moments remained vivid despite the days that had passed without them seeing each other.

Adam echoed his father's invitation. "Oh yes, stay!"

Looking down into his little face, his hazel eyes dancing with a hopeful expression, she told herself that she didn't want to disappoint him. "All right," she agreed, smiling. "But I'll have to leave right after dinner. It's a long drive back to the city."

"You could stay overnight and return in the morning," Bryce suggested.

Their eyes met. The communication between them was all the more intense because it was unspoken.

What was there about this man that drew her so, Sarah wondered. Each time she was with him, she literally yearned to touch him. She had to steel herself not to place her fingers on his arm, to press her lips against his. She felt cheated because she couldn't simply walk up to him, raise up on tiptoes, place her hands on either side of his face, and taste the sweetness of that kiss that had touched her heart in a way it had never before been touched.

Being near him, her body came alive. She was sure her color rose. Certainly her cheeks felt flushed. And her breasts tingled beneath the silken fabric of her lavender blouse.

The sexual tension made Sarah's heart flutter with anticipation and longing. She wanted to say, *yes, I'll stay the night.* But she knew it would be far too dangerous to do so. Playing with fire was one thing. But playing with fire *and* dancing on thin ice at the same time was foolhardy.

"Sorry," she declined politely. Her tone made it clear she wouldn't change her mind.

Bryce lifted one eyebrow quizzically. His expression said, "We'll see."

He continued, "We'll go into the study."

As they moved toward the study, Adam pouted at being left behind. Bryce stopped to say to him, "Tell Thaddeus there will be one more for dinner. And when Sarah and I are through with our work, you and I will take her into the winery, okay?"

Mollified, Adam responded, "Okay," then raced off toward the kitchen.

Two hours later, Sarah and Bryce had finished going over the material for the Recherché campaign in detail.

"I'm impressed," Bryce announced, leaning back in his chair and flashing a congratulatory smile at Sarah, who sat opposite him on the other side of his desk.

She had felt the work was good—more than

good—excellent. But until Bryce approved it, she couldn't help worrying. Now, she sighed with relief. "Thanks," she replied.

Watching her, he responded, "You're very good at what you do."

"I try to be."

"I guess you must enjoy it a lot."

He was probing, she knew, but she didn't mind. She answered, "I enjoy it a great deal. I wouldn't do it otherwise. Life is too short to spend it doing something you hate, something that doesn't bring a sense of fulfillment."

"I can certainly understand that. I couldn't imagine doing anything other than what I do."

"We're lucky, obviously."

He looked at her intently. "In some ways."

That was a statement with intriguing implications and Sarah had no intention of pursuing it. As she sat there quietly, she thought of Bryce's ex-wife. In order to do the work she chose, she had to leave her family. Could Bryce understand what drove her to make such a difficult choice? Probably not. Even Sarah, who could relate to this unknown woman on the basis of their shared womanhood, couldn't entirely understand how she could have done such a thing. Once that woman had made a commitment by marrying Bryce and bearing Adam, how could she then have turned her back on them?

Then Sarah realized that the alternative for that woman would have been to spend her life, or at least a large part of it, denying the work she wanted to do. That kind of sacrifice might have made life easier for Adam and Bryce, but what would it have cost her?

There are no easy answers, Sarah decided.

"You look very pensive all of a sudden," Bryce commented.

Startled, Sarah looked up at him. She *had* grown

pensive, she realized. "I think it's sheer exhaustion," she said lightly. "My whole office has been working around the clock to get this ad campaign ready."

"That's fair," Bryce said with a grin. "Everyone around here except Adam and Rex and Pancho have been working around the clock to get the Pinot Noir grapes picked, crushed, and into the fermenting tanks to make the Recherché. Your advertising genius is going to devastate our present inventory." Standing, he held out his hand to Sarah. "Enough business talk for one day. Let's walk down to the winery."

DINNER THAT EVENING WAS MARVELOUS, as Sarah knew it would be. Cream of broccoli soup followed by lemon-peppered steak and, for dessert, a sinfully rich upside-down pear cake.

As Sarah went into the living room while Bryce put Adam to bed, she felt full and tired and relaxed. It had been a lovely peaceful day. The thought of driving back to the city wasn't a pleasant one.

Still carrying the glass of wine she'd brought from the table, she walked out onto the deck. A new moon, a thin silver crescent in the sky, hung just above the shadowy treetops. It was cool out here, but not uncomfortably so.

She was so lost in the peace and quiet of Madrona that she started when Bryce said behind her, "Moonlight becomes you. It turns your hair to molten gold."

Turning to face him, she found his gaze disturbingly intense. For a moment, she hesitated, flustered. Normally she handled compliments easily. John certainly complimented her often and effusively. Yet this man's words went beyond a mere compliment. They were drenched in thinly veiled desire.

Sarah felt her pulse quicken and something odd

seemed to have happened deep in her stomach. Setting down her wine, she said awkwardly, "I...I'd better go. It's late and a long drive...."

She started to walk past him, the urgency of her feelings apparent in her hurried step. Softly, he spoke her name, "Sarah."

That one word stopped her. Her breathing became ragged and all her senses tensed expectantly.

Coming up to her, he turned her to face him. "I've thought about you every day and every night," he began, his voice husky. "I told myself that if you were cool and distant when you came, I wouldn't say anything. I know you're involved with someone else. But when I saw you, saw how you reacted to me just as I reacted to you...." He paused, then finished, "My God, how I want you."

He reached out to enfold her in his strong arms, and she stepped into his embrace as naturally as if she had done it a thousand times. Tilting her face up to his, he kissed the tip of her nose. "Sarah." He smiled down at her. Then he kissed her eyelids, which had closed. "My sweetest girl." He kissed her cheeks, then his lips grazed her earlobe and he murmured something indistinguishable but soft and inviting in her ear.

Her heart hammered wildly and her lips parted expectantly, just as his mouth covered hers, tasting, exploring, possessing.

Though she had known what was coming, she was staggered by the impact of the kiss—his lips, so demanding, her own, so yielding. Her entire body melded to his, her hands pressing against his chest, her hips resting against his. With a deep sigh, acquiescing, she gave herself up completely to him. She wanted him to come even closer, to become a part of her.

At the back of her mind was the thought, *so this is*

what a kiss is meant to be. But as soon as it came, the thought was obliterated by an overriding feeling of being swept away, drawn outside herself into a realm of pure bliss.

She was no longer in control of her body; he was. His lips commanded, and she obeyed without question. She felt his tongue caress her own, probing, inviting. She tried to summon some remnant of resistance, to pull back. But he only captured her mouth again with his own. Then his lips began to scorch a path down her throat to the wildly beating pulse at the base of it. She began to tremble. When his hands moved slowly up her arms to her shoulders, she gasped softly. His fingertips softly kneaded her shoulders beneath the thin material of her blouse.

"Don't do that, please," she begged.

Slowly, he lifted his lips from her silken throat and looked deeply into her eyes. "Don't do what?" he whispered impudently, his lips grazing her brow.

She moaned low in her throat. She wanted his touch, yearned for it. It was the only thing that could fill the terrible ache she felt inside.

Then one hand moved to where her breast was outlined through the silk of her blouse. She felt as if there were butterflies in her stomach, fluttering wildly. His fingertips began a slow sensuous circle around first one breast, then the other. The soft mounds began to quiver under his touch, and there was a tightening between her thighs.

"Please, Bryce, no," she whispered helplessly.

"Don't be afraid, sweet Sarah," he responded. Then he kissed her again, this time with less tenderness and more urgency.

A delicious languor spread through her, leaving her weak and helpless in the face of his rampant desire. She could feel every inch of his long frame pressed against her—his hard chest against her soft breasts; his taut stomach against hers; his muscled thighs against hers.

Soon she knew she wouldn't be able to resist the erotic sensations he was awakening in her. Her arms wound tightly around his neck and her fingertips caressed the silken softness of the hair at the nape of his neck.

In those brief timeless seconds, thoughts came and went. She wanted him...oh, how she wanted him! And he wanted her. What could be more natural, more right, she asked herself, before consciousness receded once more. There was only the sensation of desire, of yearning, longing, searching for this over-mastering passion and finding it.

When they finally drew apart, Sarah opened her eyes slowly. She saw Bryce looking down at her with such intense adoration that it was almost heartrending to see.

"Sarah...."

Reason returned in a blinding flash the moment he spoke her name.

She whispered in a voice that was barely in control. "I'm sorry. I shouldn't have stayed. I'm sorry."

Pausing only long enough to grab her purse and briefcase, she hurried out to her car, her eyes brimming with unshed tears. She drove a bit too fast, then forced herself to slow down. As she continued along the darkened road toward the city, toward the life she'd built, toward memories of John, she argued silently with herself.

Bryce was the type of man she had left Minnesota to get away from. He offered the kind of life she'd put behind her, a life circumscribed by tradition where her freedom to fulfill herself would be curtailed by responsibility for others. He certainly wouldn't encourage her to pursue her career as John did. He'd probably ask her to give it up.

Then there was Adam...a darling child. If his mother's heart didn't ache for him, then she must be an unfeeling bitch. But he would be a tremendous responsibility. Children need so much, Sarah knew—so much time, so much selflessness from a parent, even a stepparent. Especially from a stepparent.

No, she told herself firmly, John was right for her, not Bryce. At least for now, when there was still so much she wanted to accomplish. She wanted to test her wings, see how high she could fly. Which was exactly what John was doing, why he wouldn't entangle himself with commitments.

John is fun and my life with him is everything I ever dreamed of, Sarah said to herself. She was sure that when he returned from Hawaii they would mend their differences. They had simply been apart too long. That was why she had responded to Bryce as she did.

But an irritating little voice inside her said that these were all excuses, half-baked rationalizations to cover the painful truth. She wanted Bryce Benedict as she had never wanted any man—even John.

10

SARAH THREW HERSELF into the final preparations for the Recherché campaign. By this point she had studied the market and defined the target group—better-educated, upwardly mobile people under thirty-five who wanted a wine that would impress but still be affordable. She'd devised a slogan—So Rare...Recherché—which would be used in radio and television commercials, magazines and newspaper ads and store displays.

Still, as she worked to finalize the ad schedule, she knew that despite her expertise, Richard's artistry, and Bryce's fine product, the campaign could fail. That intangible quality, appeal, couldn't be determined for certain until the wine was on the market.

Since Bryce had approved all the facets of the campaign, Sarah had no reason to return to Madrona. They had talked over the telephone only twice. He was busy with the harvest and she was tied up with other clients as well as Recherché. She told herself she was glad they were both too involved with their respective jobs to see each other. Yet she often found herself thinking longingly of Madrona—especially that first night when Bryce had shaken her well-ordered life with one incredible kiss.

On the morning of her birthday, Sarah awoke in a dreary mood. Subconsciously she'd been aware of this milestone for the past few weeks—dreading the

day and hating herself for feeling so disquieted
about it. How could one day out of 365 be so important, she asked herself. Because, she knew, for 364
days she'd been twenty-nine. Today she was *thirty*.

Getting out of bed, she pulled on a pair of red jog-
ging pants and a sweat shirt, then laced up her running shoes. Even though she'd done the Filbert Steps
yesterday on her exercise schedule, she'd do them
again today—for good measure.

As she ran down the street to where the steps began, she thought about previous birthdays. As a
child, her birthday had been one of the happiest
days of the year. She was the center of attention
and received marvelous gifts from her family. Her
twenty-first birthday had been exciting, the official
recognition of adulthood. Even twenty-eight and
twenty-nine hadn't been bad because she was so
elated at the growing success of her business.

But thirty....

Sarah was in an uncharacteristically somber mood
when she walked into the office.

"Surprise!" Richard and Lara shouted together as
she opened the door.

Sarah shook her head dismally. "Oh no. I was
hoping nobody would remember."

"How could we forget?" Richard asked with a sly
grin. "Thirty is such a nice round number."

Sarah groaned, then laughed good-naturedly. She
was beginning to suspect that she was overreacting
to this event.

"Come on," Lara said, leading her into the tiny
room that held the Xerox machine, coffee maker and
small refrigerator. On top of the refrigerator sat a
lovely pink-and-white birthday cake. On it was
written in white icing, Happy Birthday, Boss. In the
center was one large pink candle.

"We would have put the whole thirty candles on, but I was afraid it would be a fire hazard," Richard explained with a smirk.

"Ha, ha," Sarah responded dryly.

"I thought we'd eat it after lunch," Lara added. 'By the way, *we're* treating you, for a change."

"At the Blue Fox?" Sarah quipped.

Richard laughed. "Sure. If we can have a big fat raise."

"Next month, maybe."

"In that case, we're eating at the Washington Square Bar and Grill," he replied.

It turned out to be a marvelous day, after all. Sarah's parents called to wish her a happy birthday and to say a present was in the mail. Later, her Grandfather Ericson called.

"How's my pretty little Sarah?" he asked in his mirthful booming voice. "Are you rich and famous yet?"

"No, but I'm working on it."

Suddenly she felt a fierce love for him and for all that he represented. "Oh, papa, it's so good to hear from you!"

"Are you all right, child?"

Despite her cheerfulness, something in her tone had sparked his concern.

"Oh yes," she assured him quickly. But it was only half-true. In some ways, her life was utterly perfect. But in others...well, she was just beginning to sense how unfulfilling her life was in some respects. At thirty, she had all the things she'd always thought she wanted—but now she knew those things weren't enough.

After talking to her grandfather for a few more minutes, she hung up, sighing heavily. She realized she missed him and all her family.

Just then Lara brought in the mail, and Sarah

found two birthday cards—one from Adam and another from Bryce. Adam had selected his card himself; it had a picture of a little boy holding a puppy and it read, Happy Birthday to a Special Friend. His signature was wobbly, but his own.

Bryce's card was as simple and elegant as she would have expected. It was a reproduction of a lovely Matisse painting. Inside, the card was blank. No preprinted expressions of caring from this man. Whatever sentiment he conveyed came from the heart. He wrote: "Warmest wishes for a very happy birthday. I hope your day is as beautiful as you are." It was signed, simply, "Bryce."

As Sarah sat staring at the card, Lara buzzed her.

"John's calling on line one," she said.

Sarah felt her heart sink. John. How could she talk to him as she sat there holding Bryce's card? Putting the card, along with Adam's, away in a drawer, as if John could see them through the telephone line, she picked up the receiver.

"Hi. How's Hawaii?"

"I don't know," he answered cheerfully. "Ask me how's San Francisco."

"John! You're back?"

"Yes, indeed. You think I'd miss your birthday? We can't go to Paris, as I'd planned, but at least we can go to L'Etoile."

Sarah felt dismayed. It had been so long, nearly two months. John's voice sounded familiar because they'd talked so often over the phone. But she'd almost come to view the man himself as a stranger.

"Sarah...what's wrong?"

"Nothing. I'm sorry. It's just that I wasn't expecting you back so suddenly."

"You might sound a little happier."

He sounded hurt and Sarah realized her tone had been more thoughtful than welcoming.

"I'm sorry. If I sound odd, I guess it's because I'm adjusting to turning thirty."

John laughed softly. "Take it from someone who's been there, you'll survive."

She smiled to herself. The old charm was still there. Surely, she thought, when she saw him everything would be wonderful again. If she felt awkward now, it was only because it had been so very long.

Aloud, she said, "I know. I'm still adjusting to the idea though."

"Of course. That's why I'm taking you out. The only way to handle an unwelcome birthday is to celebrate so hard you forget you're not really happy about it."

Sarah laughed. "Okay."

"I'll pick you up about seven. Bye, my lady."

As Sarah hung up, she thought about the coming evening. It would be a tremendous relief to finally see John again, she told herself, only half-believing it.

SARAH DRESSED CAREFULLY, for this evening was significant in more ways than one. The fact that she was thirty was almost beside the point. What mattered was that she would soon see John. She wore a dress he loved. It was made of aquamarine silk, with a plunging V neckline and a gold clasp at the belt. She sprayed his favorite perfume on her throat and wrists and behind her ears.

Looking at her reflection in the full-length mirror in her bedroom, she knew she looked exactly as John liked her to look—sophisticated, successful, confident. Her blond hair was pulled back in a sleek chignon, which emphasized the strong bone structure of her face—a legacy of her Swedish ancestors. The silk dress clung to her, outlining her full curves and long legs.

You'll do, she told her reflection with a wry smile. She hoped John would be pleased.

When she opened the door to admit him at seven sharp, he smiled appreciatively. And she knew she'd succeeded in looking good.

"You look even lovelier than I remembered," he said in a husky voice.

"Well, you look pretty dishy yourself," she replied.

He *did* look marvelous—even more tanned after two months in Hawaii, slightly leaner, tall, dark and handsome and beguiling. Almost too good to be true.

When he took her in his arms for a deep welcoming kiss, she caught his special scent, felt his wiry strength.

But there were no bells ringing, no fluttering of her heart.

For a moment she panicked. Then she told herself it was still too early. *Once we've been together for a while, had a chance to relax, everything will be fine*, she thought.

L'Etoile was the premier splurge in San Francisco when money was no object. Here, the socially elite partied in sumptuous surroundings. John and Sarah had a cocktail in the lounge and listened to the talented pianist play old favorites. Then they went into the rose-hued dining room. With its handsome oils on the walls, it was really more a salon than a conventional restaurant.

Sarah sensed that this place symbolized everything John was striving for—wealth, prominence, acceptance on the highest levels of society. That was why he had chosen it tonight. They ordered boned trout stuffed with a mousse of salmon and Dover sole.

As they ate, John talked of his trip, skillfully inte-

grating interesting anecdotes about his work with
vivid descriptions of Hawaii. He was an amusing
conversationalist and Sarah enjoyed listening to
him. But he didn't monopolize the conversation. He
was genuinely interested in hearing how her business was going. Sarah told him how busy she'd
been, without going into specifics. Somehow, she
was reluctant to talk about her biggest account, the
one that took up most of her time—Benedict Winery.
So she mentioned it in passing, then hurried on to
another subject.

At the end of dinner, when the waiter had cleared
the table and brought brandy and coffee, John took a
small package from his breast pocket.

"Happy birthday, my lovely lady," he said, handing her the gift.

She'd been expecting this all evening. Instead of
looking forward to it, she had felt reluctant. She
didn't feel comfortable enough with John yet to accept anything from him. But she could hardly refuse.
So she opened the gift slowly. As usual, he'd selected
something stunning, a gift that reflected his good
taste as well as a great deal of money. It was a passe-
menterie necklace in cabochon rubies and diamonds
with a Chinese silken cord.

In the past, such a breathtaking gift would have
given her tremendous pleasure. Instead she felt a
rush of sadness so intense that it was all she could
do to keep from crying then and there.

"What's wrong?" John asked. Then, trying to
lighten the somber mood, he said, "Don't tell me
you don't like rubies?"

Closing the lid of the jewelry case, Sarah set it
down on the table. Her throat felt constricted with
an emotion she didn't want to analyze.

John reached out to take her hand in his. "Sarah,
what is it?"

She looked up at him with anguished eyes. "Can you take me home, please?"

After a moment's hesitation, he answered, "Of course."

He paid the bill, then drove her back to her apartment. During the drive, she was silent. He didn't ask her again what was wrong, and she was grateful for the brief respite in the conversation. It gave her a chance to collect herself and try to sort out her turbulent emotions.

In her apartment, they sat down together on the sofa and John said, "Something happened while I was away, didn't it?"

Sarah nodded.

"You met someone else?"

"Yes." She leaned back against the pillows. "John...."

"No, Sarah, don't say anything. I don't want to know. I'm back, we're together again. That's all that matters."

Did he truly feel that way, she speculated, looking at him in astonishment. For all he knew, she might have made love with someone else. Didn't that bother him? Looking at him, she decided that it didn't.

She began, "I haven't had an affair, but...."

"Sarah, I said it doesn't matter. I've never wanted the kind of relationship where we feel we have to tell each other everything. I still feel that way."

And what would you have to tell me if I asked, she wondered.

He reached out to tilt her chin up so that she looked directly at him. "I'm just so very happy to see you again. Nothing else matters."

"John, we have to talk." There was something in her tone—a determination—that had never been there before with him.

He frowned. Rising, he walked over to the window and stood looking out. Obviously, he didn't want to have this conversation. But Sarah wasn't going to be put off. There were things that had to be said.

She continued, "We have to talk about us. That's something we haven't done very often, and it's about time we did."

"I see." He turned to look at her. "Okay, shoot."

He was reluctant, humoring her in spite of the fact he found the conversation tedious.

She said, "I've met someone who makes me question my feelings for you. But I don't want to talk about him. The real problem is *our* relationship. I'm beginning to think that I need more than you can give."

She stopped. For a moment she watched him. She had no idea how he would react to this, for she'd never made demands on him before. But his reaction, she knew, would mean the end, or a new beginning, for them.

He was silent for a very long time. Then he came back to sit beside her on the sofa, and took her hands in his. "Will you marry me?" he asked.

For a moment, she wasn't even sure she'd heard him correctly. "What did you say?"

He smiled in a self-deprecating way. "I should have put it more romantically. I should have told you how much you mean to me, how happy I am to be with you. It's all true, you know."

"But we've never talked of marriage."

"No. Obviously, it's time we did."

Had she misjudged him? She felt a surge of hope. Maybe everything could be all right between them after all.

"But, John, I didn't intend this conversation to be a demand for marriage."

"I know. That's one of the many things I like

about you. But it's clear you want our relationship to proceed to a new level, and I think you're right. It's time it did."

Her emotions were in a whirl. But somewhere deep within her she felt a misgiving. She said slowly, "Marriage is such a big step. Are you sure it's what *you* want?"

"Yes." Then he added in an offhand manner, "It won't make that big a difference in our lives."

She took a moment to consider that last statement. Unobtrusively she took her hands from his.

She thought marriage would make a very big difference in their lives. Unless... unless John expected them to continue pretty much as they had in the past. Looking at him now, Sarah was sure that was exactly what he intended.

She said in a tight voice, "I see. Things won't really change, will they? You'll still travel a great deal and I won't ask what you did while you were away."

He flashed her a surprised look.

Before he could answer, she continued, "What about children? We've never talked about that before."

"Children?" He was genuinely startled. "Why on earth would you want children? They'd play hell with our careers."

"So I take it you don't want children?" Sarah asked dryly.

"It's a moot point. I had a vasectomy some time ago."

She was stunned. Marriage was a partnership. How could John have made such an irrevocable decision alone? But after thinking about it for a moment, she understood. It was perfectly in character for John to have done such a thing.

"I see. You decided you never wanted to have children?"

"That's right. If you'd been raised in a poor family of nine kids, you'd feel the same."

Perhaps I would, she thought. But she wasn't raised in that kind of family. And she did want children. After meeting Adam, she knew that she definitely wanted children. And John could never give her any.

Sarah realized that she was faced with a clear-cut choice. Life with John would always be as it had been. Exciting. Career-oriented. Fun.

But rather empty.

There would be no real commitment, no children. Nothing to make them a family in the sense of being a close caring unit. After years of feeling that all she wanted was freedom and a stimulating career, suddenly Sarah realized those things weren't enough. She didn't by any means want to give up her career. But she wanted more than that.

Taking the jewelry case from her purse, she handed it back to John.

"It's a lovely gift and I appreciate the generous thought behind it. But I'm afraid I can't accept it." She added with a catch in her voice, "And I'm afraid I can't see you again, John."

His face looked thunderstruck. Clearly this was the last thing he expected. He was offering marriage. What more could she want?

"Sarah. . . ." He stopped, confused and hurt.

Sarah's heart went out to him. She knew he was offering all he could. It just wasn't enough.

He continued, "We've been good for each other. We make a great team! Together we can go as far as we both want to go."

"In our careers, yes. But my career is only part of my life. And I'm beginning to think it isn't the most fulfilling part."

"I don't understand."

"No." Her voice was soft with the sad realization that John would never comprehend what she needed from him. "We want different things from life, John. I'm not saying what you want is wrong. I understand why you want it so. But it isn't right for me."

"Sarah." His hurt confused look spoke volumes. *I've been everything any woman could want,* he seemed to say. *Generous, thoughtful, supportive of your work.*

He had been all those things, Sarah knew.

She reached out to stroke his cheek lovingly. She cared for him. She always would, in a way. But not in the way a lifetime commitment required. After knowing Bryce, she realized that now.

"I'm sorry," she whispered.

But she couldn't help smiling inwardly at this scenario. For all the time she'd been with John, she'd been half-afraid he would leave her for someone else. His lack of commitment always made that a very real possibility. Now, he was offering marriage, and she was turning him down. *She* was leaving him.

She felt no surge of ego at the thought. She was deeply sad that a relationship that had been so good in so many ways, finally wasn't quite good enough.

To John's credit, he didn't argue further. He looked at her helplessly, and she felt a rush of tender concern for him. Part of her would always care for him, for he was her first mature love.

But when he left, she felt relief mingle with her sadness and sense of loss. For a long time she'd been lying to herself, telling herself that John was all she wanted, that she could live with the limits of their relationship. Finally, she was being honest with herself. And though it hurt, it felt good in a way.

Inevitably, Bryce came into her thoughts. That strong quiet man had turned her life around. And she knew that whatever happened between them, she would never again be the same.

Turning out the lamps, she stood looking at the clear sky full of stars and the city glittering with its myriad lights. Red, blue, green, yellow neon lights flickered off and on, streetlamps strung patterns across the city as did the lights on the Bay Bridge. All that glitter and glowing was like candles on a birthday cake. *My birthday cake,* she told herself, and smiled remembering Richard's comment about thirty candles constituting a fire hazard.

It had been quite a birthday. *I was right to think of it as a milestone,* she said silently. It had certainly been that. Treating herself to one last appreciative sweep of her "view," Sarah turned away and found herself recalling Bryce's handwritten words: "Warmest wishes for a very happy birthday. I hope your day is as beautiful as you are."

Her heart sang happy birthday.

11

IN THE MIDDLE OF OCTOBER, just a week before Re-cherché was to be released, Sarah went once more to Madrona. The ad campaign was complete—the commercials produced and scheduled for radio and television, the brochures printed and ready for distribution, the newspaper and magazine ads already placed.

She came to Madrona now to give Bryce some brochures for the party. At least, that was the official reason for her visit. The real reason, she knew, was to see him. Now that she was no longer involved with John, she was curious to see what her reaction to Bryce would be.

From the time she'd reached the Sonoma turnoff, she'd been caught in the harvest traffic. A procession of pickup trucks pulling grape-filled gondolas had delayed her. When she finally turned onto the narrow country road and reached the redwood sign of Benedict Winery, she felt her pulse accelerate and a smile curve her mouth.

As she drove up the hill and through the winery area, she was amazed at the frenzy of activity. It was just before twelve o'clock and the pickers had not yet stopped for lunch.

Near the crest of the hill, a gondola heaped high with Sauvignon Blanc grapes was being hooked to a truck so it could be pulled to the winery. Two pickers, carrying lug boxes of the grapes, spilled their harvest onto the load, smiled and returned her wave as they headed back down the vineyard.

Autumn reds and golds were beginning to color the countryside. Even the air carried the scent of the ripe grapes and newly fermenting wine. It was an absolutely beautiful day, Sarah observed, happy to be here.

As she pulled up in front of the house, she saw Bryce and another man walking toward her. Stepping from her car, she waved, and Bryce waved back. By the time he reached her, his face was suffused with a smile of such transparent adoration that she felt overcome with the force of his feeling. Her own response was just as strong.

I want him, she told herself vehemently. *I want him so much.*

Then, concerned that her feelings might be embarrassingly obvious to the stranger walking beside Bryce, she forced her expression to turn cordial but circumspect.

"Sarah, this is Tomas Carlino, a neighbor. Tomas, this is Sarah Montgomery."

The balding middle-aged man extended his hand to her. "Ah, yes. The young woman who is going to make your wine famous. I am most happy to meet you, Miss Montgomery."

"Benedict Vintage Recherché is fine enough to speak for itself," Sarah replied, shaking his hand. "It needs no help from me. I'm simply going to make people aware of it."

Tomas laughed and his dark eyes sparkled with merriment. "Very good. It is the wine itself that matters. And here we have the finest wine in the world."

"Tomas, old friend, your problem is a lack of confidence." Bryce's sly good humor spoke well for their friendship.

"But it's the simple truth. You know, Miss Montgomery, migratory birds fly as much as five hundred miles off course just to eat our grapes. Mostly my Cabernet Sauvignon grapes.''

Sarah laughed with Bryce and Mr. Carlino's over-weening pride. But, actually, she was charmed by him.

"Bees too, you know. Has anyone told you that bees test our grapes the same as the birds do?" he continued, obviously enjoying himself.

"I have heard that birds, especially starlings, eat a fair part of the crop, but bees...?" She looked questioningly at Bryce.

Before he could answer, his friend said, "Bees are almost as good an indicator as birds for when the grapes are ready. Why just a few minutes ago, while Bryce and I were testing the east slope, I saw a bee, drunk as a lord, fall right off a cluster of his Sauvignon Blanc. Those grapes looked ready to burst with sugar." Then he winked at her and another jolly smile brightened his face. "Bees don't bother with sour grapes, you know."

"Enough, Tomas, of this foolishness. Come, lunch is ready, I'm sure. And Adam and Thaddeus will not forgive us if we keep Sarah out here any longer."

Lunch was delicious, which did not surprise Sarah. There were several guests, some she'd met and others new to her. All were associated with the harvest in one way or another. It was a happily confusing time with constant telephone interruptions for several of the guests, as well as for Bryce. The conversation centered on vines, grapes, weather, the crush—it was as if there was nothing else to be considered. Adam was unusually subdued and as soon as he had eaten he asked his father to excuse him. Thaddeus took the opportunity to tell Bryce he'd promised to take Adam with him up to Wolf House that afternoon.

Bryce had to take another telephone call before he

could reply. He returned to the table just as Thaddeus asked Sarah if she'd ever been to the ruins of Jack London's home. "It's in Glen Ellen, only about fifteen minutes from here...as the crow flies. I've been reading—telling—Adam *Call of the Wild.* I have to soften much of the story, but since Adam loves Rex so, I think he's getting something out of it. At least, he listens attentively."

Sarah told him she had visited there a number of times. "I find it all fascinating."

"Come with us then. By the time we get back, Bryce and Tomas will have finished their business."

"Yes, please stay, Sarah," Bryce insisted. "Tomas and I won't be very long. Then I'll be free—" He grinned as the telephone rang again. "Don't bother, Thaddeus, it'll be for me."

ARRIVING AT THE Jack London State Park, Sarah pulled into a parking space. They walked up the path toward a knoll surrounded by redwood, Douglas fir, oak and shedding cinnamon-barked madrona trees. "House of Happy Walls," said Thaddeus, gesturing toward the large fieldstone house that was now a museum and housed London's memorabilia. "His widow, Charmian, built it as a memorial to him. He died in 1916 at age forty. She built the house in 1919 and lived there alone until she died in 1955 at age eighty-four. That's a long time to live with a memory, isn't it?"

Sarah thought Thaddeus meant the comment as a rhetorical question, so she did not reply. But she asked herself if perhaps he lived with hard memories. Thaddeus was so good with Adam, it seemed too bad that he did not have a family. And he was an interesting man—obviously one of many talents. She wondered again why he did not have a life of his own.

They continued on their way to the ruins of Wolf House. Sarah kept trying to engage Adam in conversation, and while he responded to her questions, he kept an emotional distance between himself and her. He was not unfriendly, just cool.

The afternoon was still bright and sunny, but a breeze had begun to blow through the dry grasses and ripple the Spanish moss that hung over the branches of the oaks.

They walked along a path that followed the contours of the land up the rolling hills and down along a creek. Clumps of live oak, cedar, pine and fir grew everywhere. Much of the grounds were not cleared, but were a tangle of brush and low-hanging limbs. There were some open spaces, small meadows, covered now with dry bleached-out grass. An occasional fruit tree cropped up with no apparent reason for it being in that particular place. Sarah thought it likely that someone had just decided a flowering almond or peach tree would add a spot of beauty in the spring when it blossomed or in the fall when its leaves would turn the golden yellow of autumn.

When they reached a bench by the turn of the creek, Sarah suggested they sit a minute. "Adam, you're very quiet today." she said.

"I know it," he replied.

Sarah waited for him to expand on the comment, but he did not.

Continuing their walk, they followed the path down a long slope and up another. Suddenly they came upon a clearing, and beyond a large stand of trees were the ruins of Wolf House. Even though she'd been here before, Sarah was impressed. The setting was magnificent and so must have been the house. The walls, built of volcanic lava boulders, still outlined the four-storey structure.

They climbed the steps of the risers, built for visitors, and studied the floor plan of the house. Fifteen thousand square feet, twenty-six rooms, nine fireplaces. The vision of Jack London had been a bold one. He'd meant this dwelling to stand for a thousand years and quarter generations of his descendants. The house had been deliberately fired just before he and his wife were to occupy it. How sad, Sarah thought, looking over the ruins. The edges of the stone structure had been softened first by the terrible fire, then by moss and grass and time.

Sarah and Thaddeus followed the exterior outline of the house, while Adam executed the steps of the risers...up and down, up and down, his mood and demeanor still pensive.

"It's a shame, isn't it?" Sarah said. "Imagine building all this and having it go up in smoke just when it was ready for you."

"Yes. This is a bittersweet place—so many dreams were wrapped up in this house. Unfulfilled dreams. I find it very stimulating creatively. I often come here alone and work on my poetry."

"Mmm, you're an interesting man, Thaddeus. I'd love to hear something you've written. Would you recite one of your poems?"

He turned quickly toward her, beaming happily. "Would I? My dear, you should understand the creative temperament better than to even ask. Of course, I'd be happy to show off a bit." He pondered his choices a moment, then shrugged. "This one's called 'Indiscretion.'"

He quoted:

In venomous haste
    to hurl spears of hate,
We forgot tomorrow.
Accusing,
    we recanted vows of love.

Now tomorrow is today,
    and we walk gingerly
        on a crust
Of bitterness.

Thaddeus's voice had dropped to almost a whisper by the end of the poem. In the silence that followed, Sarah, touched by the content and his poignant recitation, realized Thaddeus had just told her something rather important about himself.

She was grateful that she and John had terminated their relationship without recrimination and bitterness.

"That was written quite some time ago...commemorating my Waterloo, so to speak. This one I call 'Fragmented.'" He paused, looking out across the clearing as if distancing himself. Then, in a hushed but absolutely flat voice, recited:

There is a duplicity
About the heart.
Oft' times
When it should sing
And leap—
It only
Weeps.

At that moment, Sarah felt a strong kinship with Thaddeus. Looking at him, she saw that his expression was pensive.

"Thaddeus—they're lovely. But so sad...." She left the thought unfinished. She wanted to say more...ask more.

"Yes," he responded. "When I wrote those two, I'd learned a hard lesson. Sometimes we recognize too late exactly what it is we want."

As much as she wanted to ask him about that

revealing statement, Sarah knew it would be an unwarrantable invasion of privacy. Whatever he wanted to say to the world had been said in his poems. Anything else he kept hidden in his heart.

"You're quite remarkable, Thaddeus," she said sincerely.

He smiled, banishing the sadness from his countenance. "I like to think so. I'm your basic educated ex-hippie turned country philosopher." He sighed and shook his head. "Thirty years ago when I was haunting coffeehouses I never would have dreamed I would end up like this—settled, more or less a pillar of society, a traditionalist."

Sarah smiled. "But you like your present life."

"Oh, it's a wonderful life. That's the ironic part. Perhaps time does change all things eventually."

Sarah thought of the solid traditional people who had reared her. She felt a pang of homesickness such as she'd never before experienced. It was not just a prickle of remembering, it was a hard jolt of loving them, wanting to touch base with them. *Maybe Thaddeus is right,* she thought. *Time changes all things.*

Suddenly Adam shouted from far away, "Thaddeus! Sarah! Come here."

"How peremptory he can be at times," Thaddeus said. "I think five-year-olds have a Henry VIII complex—they think they rule the world."

"Thaddeus! Sarah!" Adam shouted again, exasperated at their slowness.

"I'll see what he wants," Sarah told Thaddeus, who was leaning comfortably against a large rock.

"Thanks, Sarah. I'm not into romps as I was at thirty."

When she reached Adam he was sitting watching the breeze bend the grass. As she approached, he said simply, "There's some ants here," pointing to a large number of scurrying insects.

"Yes, I see." Sarah knelt down beside the brown-haired child and looked at the rotted limb of a fallen tree. "Those are carpenter ants. They're called that because they work in wood." She looked at Adam to see if he had any response to make.

He continued to stare at the ants and did not acknowledge her comments in any way.

"It's good they're all just running this way and that," she continued. "I've read that when a storm's coming, ants march in a straight line. Do you think that's true?"

He shrugged his small shoulders, then turning to face her, said, "You didn't come back for a long time."

Sarah caught her breath. So...he'd lost trust in their friendship again. "I had a lot of work to get done. Launching your dad's wine was a hurry-up job. But I thought about you."

He cut his eyes first one way, then the other, obviously considering what she'd said. Then he looked directly at her, a miniature of Bryce. The same hazel eyes appearing to change color as his emotions altered his mood. Suddenly a brightness appeared in them and he smiled up at her.

Sarah felt that tug at her heart again. It was beginning to be a familiar feeling when she was with this child.

The breeze gusted across the meadow and Sarah felt as if it beckoned. "Adam, would you like to race the wind with me?"

He nodded and took her hand. They ran across the opening toward the path, which wound around a large cedar tree. When they were almost there, Adam turned and held up his arms to Sarah. She swooped him up and spun around and around.

Leaning back in her arms, Adam laughed with the joy that only a five-year-old can express with such a bubbling chortle. Then he clasped his arms tightly around her neck and began to whisper her name. "Sarah...Sarah...Sarah," she heard him breathe into her ear.

Alternating with him, she began to chant his name. "Adam...Adam...Adam...." Spinning one last time, she reached the path and stepped directly in front of Bryce who stood leaning against the trunk of the large cedar.

He caught the two of them in his arms, steadying her as she regained her balance.

Sarah, still holding Adam tightly in her arms, his small face hard against her own, looked up at Bryce and saw clearly what this tableau said to him. It was all there in his expressive eyes. Just as it had been a few minutes earlier in Adam's.

But Bryce did not cut his eyes from side to side, avoiding her glance as Adam had before she said the magic words—I thought about you. That was the difference between the wary child and the confident man.

Sarah's brain registered the tumultuous cadence of heartbeats; Adam's from exertion and happiness, hers from that and more. And Bryce's? Thaddeus's poem came to mind..."should sing and leap." At this moment, there was no duplicity about Bryce Benedict's heart. It was singing. It was leaping. She could feel it beating its joy for this moment.

When they rejoined Thaddeus back at the steps at Wolf House, Bryce explained he needed a break too. Tossing a set of keys to Thaddeus, he said, "You can take Adam home in the Jeep. I'll catch a ride with Sarah."

"I don't want to go home, dad," Adam protested. "Sarah and I are having fun."

Bryce smiled warmly, but his tone was firm. "No

arguing.'' When Adam glanced at Sarah, Bryce continued, ''Sarah will be here for a long time yet. We'll talk her into staying for dinner.''

Adam brightened. ''Really? Will you stay, Sarah?''

Sarah hesitated. She hadn't planned to spend the day here. On the other hand, she had absolutely no desire to return to the city right now.

''Okay,'' she agreed. ''I'll stay.''

Adam let out a childish whoop of glee, then turned to go with Thaddeus.

When Sarah and Bryce were alone, he said with belated concern, ''I just remembered this is Saturday. I hope I'm not spoiling any plans you may have had.''

''No. I didn't have any plans.''

As they stood there together, neither speaking, she realized that she had to say something about John. She knew that was who Bryce was referring to when he spoke of plans she may have had.

She explained briefly, ''Nowadays, I'm what you might call unencumbered. I'm no longer involved with John.''

''I won't pretend to be unhappy about that,'' Bryce said quickly. ''May I ask what happened?''

''I just... just realized that I didn't care for him in the way I thought I did.''

''And what exactly made you come to that realization, Sarah?''

He had moved closer now. Though she had turned to look at the ruins of the house, she wasn't really seeing it. She was intensely aware of Bryce standing so near. She could smell his special scent, hear his breathing, sense his green-brown eyes watching her intently.

What had made her realize she didn't love John?

Bryce, of course. Bryce, who made her pulse race, who touched something profound in her that John had never even recognized.

"I'm sorry," Bryce said, his voice husky. "If you'd rather not talk about it...."

"It isn't that. I'm not upset about it. In fact, I feel quite relieved, in a way," Sarah admitted. It was true, and she couldn't pretend otherwise. After feeling torn for two months, it was a relief to have made a decision and to know it was the right one.

She didn't feel anger toward John. In many ways, their relationship had been good for both of them for a long time. Through John's encouragement, Sarah had found the strength to start her own business. And they'd had fun together—there were memories that Sarah would always cherish. But it was all definitely in the past. John wasn't her future. She knew that now.

"I can understand feeling relieved," Bryce commented.

Looking at him, Sarah watched his countenance cloud. She sensed somehow that he was thinking of his ex-wife. Overcome with curiosity about the woman, she couldn't resist saying, "I get the feeling you've gone through a similar situation."

His smile was wry, but not bitter. "Oh yes." Then looking at her, he said candidly, "I think I'd better tell you about Melissa."

"You don't have to," Sarah offered, hoping he would.

He reached out and cupped her chin in one hand, tilting her face so he could look directly into her eyes. "I think I do. I want to." He released her and, taking a clean handkerchief from his pocket, spread it on the nearby riser. "Sit here," he suggested, and made himself comfortable beside her.

"We married too young," he began. "She was

eighteen, I was twenty-two. She wasn't a local girl. She came at spring vacation, visiting a cousin. I was home from school. It was what's known as a whirl-wind courtship. We whirled into marriage. The wedding was a technicolor production. We never took time to decide what we wanted in life, discuss our values, plans, needs." He shrugged and shook his head. "But it wasn't anyone's fault. Certainly not Melissa's. We were simply too young...and didn't know ourselves well enough."

Sarah understood perfectly. When she and Kenny had discussed marriage, it was the same—in a way. They had planned how they would decorate their apartment, go on a honeymoon. They didn't discuss careers, having children, money.

"I was twenty-five when I left Minneapolis," she told him. "I decided I was too young for marriage then. At least, that was the excuse I used. But eighteen...."

"I know. That's still a child. Twenty-two wasn't much older. I still had graduate work to do. Melissa was a very bright girl—and in many ways, more a woman than a girl. We both had a lot of growing up to do. And we didn't grow in the same direction. By the time of our tenth anniversary we were com-pletely different people who had almost nothing in common—not even the love we'd originally felt for each other existed by then."

"How sad," Sarah said gently.

"Yes. For both of us. When Melissa didn't get pregnant early in our marriage, she decided to start college. I was doing my graduate work at the same time. We lived just off campus. And then she got very caught up in it. She discovered that she loved archaeology and was already talking about going off on a dig when she finally got pregnant with Adam. I hoped a baby would bring us closer, but it didn't."

"No. When you're so far apart, I don't think a baby can help. Babies create new problems, they don't solve old ones."

Bryce smiled tenderly down at Sarah. "How did you get to be so knowledgeable?"

"Well, I don't know everything." Her grin was rueful. "I've just always felt that having children should be a joy and a privilege, not an accident."

"Exactly. Melissa hated being pregnant, but I assumed her feelings would change once the baby came. She *did* love Adam, you know. And she was a good mother—to a point. But she was determined that he wouldn't stop her from fulfilling her dream of working on a dig. To make a long story short, we got a divorce, she gave me custody of Adam, and left."

"Does she have any contact with Adam?"

"Yes. She writes regularly and calls at Christmas and on his birthday. As I said, I honestly believe she loves him. But she isn't committed to him. She's committed to her career."

"Funny—I know a lot of fathers like that," Sarah commented, not bothering to soften the bluntness of her statement.

Bryce flashed her a startled look, then smiled. "I guess you're right. I just can't understand anyone— a father or mother—walking away from a child."

"Nor can I."

For a moment they were both quiet. It was a comfortable silence. Sarah looked around the ruins of the once-great house in its magnificent setting. Inexplicably she thought of when she and John were here last year. They'd had their one blockbuster of a quarrel. John had been fascinated with the architectural concepts of the house and when she'd tried to share some of *her* feelings about being in this place where the writer she felt so familiar with had lived, he'd been first preoccupied, then annoyed. Stung by his abrupt rejection of her interest with "you know I don't read fiction," she told him she'd make very sure she wouldn't bore him with further discussion. She'd left the site and returned to the car in the parking lot.

Later, in Sonoma, over a glass of wine, they'd made up. Much later, in her apartment, they'd made love. Afterward John had held her close and whispered, "It's all right that we're so different in our interests... opposites attract, you know."

Now enjoying the companionable silence she felt with this man, Sarah thought—true, there's attraction in being opposites. A certain excitement in the challenge. But there's also attrition. And *that* can get old in a hurry.

She turned away from looking at the house and let her gaze travel over the forested terrain and up toward the mountains across the way. The October afternoon was pure Indian summer, golden and tranquil. When she glanced at Bryce she saw he was watching her. She felt closer to him at that moment than she'd ever felt with John. In a moment, she thought, he would take her in his arms and kiss her.

And she would respond. How *would* she respond? She wanted to share every intimacy with him, both physical and emotional. But there were problems. And there weren't easy solutions to those problems.

"Sarah...."

His voice was a caress. Her body responded, but her mind held her back. "No," she whispered. "Don't say anything else. Not right now."

He hesitated. She could see what an effort of will it took for him not to gather her forcefully into his arms.

Finally, he said, "All right. I won't say anything else *yet*."

He reached out to tilt her chin up with one long finger. When her eyes were locked into his, he leaned toward her, ever so slowly, still holding her gaze. When his face was so close to hers that she could feel his breath upon her skin and see the tiny crescent-shaped scar at the left side of his lower lip, he sighed her name and wrapped her in an affectionate embrace.

He simply held her, gently...tenderly. As she rested against him, enfolded in caring it seemed to her, she felt her eyes brim with tears. Happy tears, she told herself.

Then he sighed, deeply this time, the way one does when finally at ease. Releasing her, he took her face between his hands and touched her lips with his own, then said, "Someday, soon, I won't let you run away from what's between us."

EARLY ON THE EVENING of October twenty-eighth, Sarah
arrived at Madrona for the party introducing Recherché. It was to be a formal affair and she had
dressed accordingly in her very best. At her ears and
around her throat were pearls, not a gift from John,
but jewelry she'd bought to celebrate her first year of
healthy profit in her business. She wore a long white
silk sheath, high-necked and slit provocatively up
both sides. Over it was a flowing quilted silk jacket
in a bold red-and-black Chinese print. With her hair
pulled back in a sleek chignon, she looked sophisticated and lovely.

Richard, Ginger and Lara were coming together.
They'd invited her to ride with them, but she had
declined, using the excuse that she would want to
talk to Bryce after the party. She'd even packed an
overnight bag, and brought it along.

The nervousness that made her hand fumble as
she reached for the doorbell wasn't entirely due to
the significance of the premiere. In a moment she
would see Bryce for the first time since that afternoon at Wolf House. No matter what happened tonight with Recherché, she suspected Bryce wouldn't
be as patient with her as he had been.

Thaddeus opened the door and smiled at her
warmly.

"May I say you look lovely, Sarah?"

She smiled. "You may, indeed. And thank you."

"Bryce is in his office. Why don't you go into the

living room and I'll let him know you've arrived."

"Am I the first?"

"Yes. The others will come any moment."

"Sarah!"

She turned to find Adam smiling at her. "Gosh, you look pretty!"

She knelt down to look him straight in the eye. "Why, thank you, sir. Are you coming to the party?"

"No," Thaddeus answered for him. Flashing a stern look at Adam, he added, "You know you're supposed to be in bed, young man."

After a brief argument, Adam finally went off to his room.

Staring after the small dejected figure, Thaddeus sighed. "Poor little thing. He doesn't understand. While this may be called a party, it's actually a very serious occasion."

"Yes," Sarah agreed. She knew as well as anyone what was riding on the success or failure of Recherché. It meant the difference between Benedict Winery remaining a fine but small entity, or joining the big league of well-known, highly regarded winemakers.

"Well, make yourself comfortable."

Thaddeus headed toward the office and Sarah went into the living room. She found a table draped in white linen. On it were several bottles of Recherché in silver ice buckets. Eyeing the labels critically, Sarah decided that Richard had truly done a terrific job. But what mattered, she knew, was the wine itself. The wine experts who would be tasting it for the first time tonight wouldn't care how it was packaged. Their professional opinions of the wine could make or break it.

"Sarah."

She turned at the sound of the husky voice that

had the power to make her heart melt. Bryce stood in the doorway. He was dressed in a black tuxedo and white tucked shirt. The formal clothes fit his broad shoulders and tapering hips becomingly. And he wore them with an ease few men could match.

Again, Sarah thought what a magnificent physical presence he had, whether in work clothes or formal attire. It came, she decided, from being master of all he surveyed—including being master of her heart. *I love him,* she told herself.

Her voice seemed to be caught somewhere in her throat.

"You look gorgeous," he said. The warmth of his admiring smile was reflected in his hazel eyes.

She flushed, then pulling herself together, quipped, "You're rather gorgeous yourself."

He laughed. "Sarah, you're thoroughly unpredictable."

Just then the doorbell rang and Sarah heard Thaddeus's footsteps cross the hall to answer it.

It was Vince and his wife. They'd come a minute early for reinforcement, Vince teased as he shook Bryce's hand. Laughing, Bryce bent to kiss the attractive young woman's cheek, then began the introductions.

"Sarah, this is Beth...." As the doorbell chimed again he shrugged and said, "Well, you two get acquainted. God, I can't wait for this evening to end."

But it didn't end until the wee hours of the morning.

Later, thinking back on the evening, Sarah saw it as a kaleidoscope of people, conversations, actions and reactions. Tomas Carlino, among other vintners, was there, praising Recherché. "It's *almost* as good as my Cabernet Sauvignon," he declared with a twinkle in his dark eyes.

"If you'll admit that much, you must secretly

think it's just as good," Bryce responded with a laugh.

"That may be true, but I'll never say so," Tomas answered.

As each of the half-dozen critics who'd been invited arrived, Bryce spoke to them, explaining the history of Recherché. Then he offered them a glass. When the first critic said he liked it, Sarah felt a slight lessening of the tension that filled the room, despite the aura of gaiety. When the second critic agreed, she breathed a deep sigh of relief. When the third critic declared Recherché to be the best buy for the money, even Bryce began to relax. Because the wine was a huge success, the party was also. As the evening wore on, the tension dissolved and was replaced with genuine good cheer. Bryce was the center of attention, as both the wine critics and other vintners questioned him about Recherché's delicacy and balance.

When Richard, Ginger and Lara arrived, Sarah brought them over to Bryce.

"I'm very pleased you came," Bryce said, shaking Richard's hand. "You've done a marvelous job."

"Well, I had a fine product to work with. I must say, I'm as impressed with your house as I am with your wine."

Bryce smiled proudly. "Thanks. Feel free to wander around and look it over. I'd give you a guided tour, but I'm a bit busy."

At that moment another wine critic arrived, and Bryce had to excuse himself. While Sarah stood chatting and sipping Recherché with Richard, Ginger and Lara, part of her attention remained on Bryce across the room.

Thaddeus had prepared a sumptuous buffet, but he employed temporary help to do the serving. To-

night, he too was host, along with Bryce. He clearly
had a certain standing in the community, for he was
greeted warmly by the guests, as was Bryce. Some of
the women, in particular, seemed quite taken with
Thaddeus. He might not have his own true love, but
neither was he celibate.

To Sarah's amusement, Lara flirted outrageously
with Thaddeus, and he reciprocated with élan.

There was one poignant moment between Bryce
and Thaddeus, which Sarah happened to observe.
The two men were standing apart from the other
guests at one point and raised their glasses in a silent
toast, seemingly to each other. But Sarah sensed that
it was to Luis, who'd conceived Benedict Vintage
Recherché.

Then Art and Shari Lauffer arrived. Bryce intro-
duced Sarah to Shari and the four of them stood
talking for a while. When Bryce was called away by
another wine critic, Art said, "I take it Recherché is
a big success?"

"Yes," Sarah answered, unable to contain a big
smile. "It's such a relief after all these weeks of
working and worrying."

The three of them were jostled by some people
heading toward the buffet table.

"Let's get out of this madhouse," Art suggested.
He grabbed an open bottle of Recherché from the
table and three glasses, then led Sarah and Shari into
Bryce's den.

"Whew! What a crowd," Art said. Sitting down
behind Bryce's desk, he poured wine for each of
them. Raising his glass in a toast, he said, "To
Recherché."

"And to Stoney Creek Inn," Sarah added.

"That reminds me," Shari said after taking a sip of
wine. "Art tells me you're in advertising. Judging

from the successful way you've promoted Recherché, maybe we should get your help with our inn."

"I'd love to work on it," Sarah responded enthusiastically. "Tell me about the place."

"It's a big old Victorian farmhouse with a parlor, huge dining room, maids' quarters and eight bedrooms. We're going to turn the maids' quarters into an office and bedroom for our use and furnish the parlor, dining room, and bedrooms in antiques that would also be offered for sale. There's a big old barn too, that I thought we could use for something, though I'm not sure what."

"Why not turn it into an antique shop?" Sarah suggested. "It sounds like you're into antiques."

Shari, who was red-haired and freckled like her husband, grinned broadly. "What a neat idea! Why didn't I think of that?"

"If you handle it right," Sarah continued, "you can make your inn an exclusive intimate little place that will have reservations booked months in advance."

"Now *that* appeals to me," Art said. "I've been a little afraid that this inn business might be a turkey, financially speaking."

"Oh, I don't think it will be," Sarah assured him. "The wine country's so popular, and people love to stay in authentic old places that offer terrific food. Judging from your restaurant, I'm sure you can handle the terrific food requirement."

Sarah thoughtfully sipped her wine and wondered how the Lauffers managed to combine country and city life. Finally she decided to be direct. "How do you manage being in two places at one time, so to speak?"

"It ain't easy."

"No big deal." They spoke in unison, then laughed.

"Which is it?" Sarah asked. "Do you stay in the city most of the time? Do you commute?"

Art explained that until recently they lived in their apartment in San Francisco. But now that there were at least livable quarters in the farmhouse, Shari was spending part of each week up here. "You know," he finished, "it's only about an hour's drive. Lots of commuters spend more than an hour going to and from work."

Shari reached over to take his hand. "Sometimes he surprises me and drives up after the restaurant closes."

Sarah observed the love between the two of them confirmed in the soft shining look in their eyes. Absence makes the heart grow fonder, she thought.

They talked for several more minutes about their plans, and then Art and Shari made an appointment to come to Sarah's office the next week.

When they went back into the living room to rejoin the party, Sarah felt exhilarated. Promoting this inn would be a labor of love, as Recherché had been. More than that, though, the Lauffers interest in her professionally verified what she'd begun to feel earlier that evening. She was good at what she did. Extremely good, in fact.

It was immensely reassuring to get such positive feedback about her abilities.

Later, Sarah came to the buffet table to get something to eat finally, when she heard a low rustling sound. Glancing down, she saw a tiny hand reach up at one end of the table, grab a bite-size quiche, then disappear. After a moment the hand reappeared, dropped the quiche on the table, then moved cautiously along the edge of the table until it encountered some petit fours. Grasping one of the small cakes, the hand disappeared once more.

Walking closer, Sarah bent down to peer under the tablecloth. She came face to face with Adam, who was about to take a bite of a petit four.

Startled, he nearly dropped his bounty. Then he grinned impishly.

"Aren't you supposed to be in bed?" Sarah asked the pajama-clad figure.

He nodded. "I got hungry," he explained. "Thaddeus wouldn't let me have any of this stuff today."

"Mmm. He probably didn't want to spoil your appetite for dinner."

"But dinner's over. And I'm *starving*."

"Tell you what. I'll make up a plate for you and bring it into your bedroom. But you have to go back there pronto."

Adam grinned and began to crawl out from under the table.

"Okay," he said as he scuttled away, making certain not to be seen.

Sarah put some hors d'oeuvres on a plate, then turning toward Adam's bedroom, found Bryce watching her. He'd seen the culprit. He looked deliberately at the food she held, then at her. Grinning, one eyebrow lifted in amusement, he shrugged as if to say, "Why not?" Sarah winked and duplicated his shrug.

In his room, Adam was sitting up in bed with the bedside lamp on, waiting impatiently. Sarah sat down on the end of the bed, and watched while he happily munched on the goodies she'd brought.

Suddenly remembering his manners he said between bites, "Thanks. I *was* starving."

Sarah laughed. "I doubt that. You hardly look all skin and bones to me."

When Adam had finished every crumb on the plate, Sarah set it on the nightstand, then tucked him in.

"Get to sleep, you little rascal."

He grinned up at her. At that instant he looked so utterly appealing that she wanted to take him in her arms and kiss him good-night, to smooth his ruffled hair and tell him she loved him. For she did love him, she knew. But something held her back. Somehow, she knew that to get too close to him before she was sure she would remain in his life, would be unfair to him.

So she simply said, "Good night, Adam," and withdrew, turning out the lamp and closing the door behind her.

IT WAS LONG PAST MIDNIGHT and Sarah was standing alone, nibbling on an hors d'oeuvre. She listened as, a few feet away, the wine critic from one of the San Francisco newspapers assured Bryce, "You'll make a fortune from Recherché."

As if sensing that she was watching him, Bryce turned toward her and for a moment their glances locked. We've done it, he seemed to say. The look of gratitude—and something much more—made her heart soar. In that moment of silent communication, Sarah knew that this night would not end with the departure of the last guest. On this night, she and Bryce would make love.

She wasn't sure how she knew this. But she was as certain of it as if he had said aloud, 'Stay with me tonight."

A tenseness she'd felt for some time now dissolved. The caution she'd held onto had been self-protective. To relinquish that shield now was almost a physical experience. She felt no awkwardness, only a quiet acceptance of what was surely meant to be. Why else was she here in this place, at this time?

From the beginning of her involvement with John, she'd not trusted the future of their relationship enough to expect a committed intimacy. She'd not demanded, so she couldn't be refused. She'd always held back a part of herself.

She had known Bryce only two months, yet there was a kindred familiarity between their spirits that united their hearts. And this had been so from the first day they'd met.

He's the reason I chose San Francisco five years ago, she thought, *and not Los Angeles, Chicago or New York,* which she'd seriously considered. He was her lodestone.

She had always found magnets and magnetism fascinating. She was especially intrigued by magnes lapis, the black stone that stuck to the iron tip of the legendary shepherd's staff.

But scientific reasoning didn't really matter, she thought now. Love's intuitive power guided her. Desire flowed through her entire being — heart, soul and body. Desire born of love, its promise as rich as the sparkling Recherché wine.

That internal needle Sarah had always felt within herself, spun as if magnetized to Bryce. She belonged with this man. It was that simple.

And soon, she knew, she would be part of him and he of her.

13

THE PARTY WAS OVER. The last guest had finally departed, taking with him a complimentary bottle of Benedict Vintage Recherché.

Richard, Ginger and Lara had long since left for the drive back to the city. Art and Shari had gone to their farmhouse nearby.

When Thaddeus started to tidy up the messy living room, Bryce said, "Leave it. It's late and I know you must be exhausted. You've cooked and cleaned for days preparing for this. Tomorrow will be soon enough to clean up the mess."

Thaddeus sighed. "I hate to admit it, but I *am* a bit tired. Good night, Bryce, Sarah. And congratulations to both of you on a job well done."

Finally, they were alone.

Sarah felt all her carefully acquired sophistication leave her. She was nineteen again, nervous, unsure. She looked everywhere but at Bryce. And a funny lump seemed to have come into her throat.

She wondered what was wrong. She was not a trembling virgin. What happened to all that readiness she'd felt such a short time ago?

But she *was* trembling—with a combination of nervousness and anticipation that sent a delicious thrill up her spine.

"Sarah."

She looked up and saw Bryce holding out his hand toward her. Walking up to him slowly, she took it, and he led her out onto the deck.

The October night was cool and clear. A huge orange moon hung low on the horizon, surrounded by diamond-bright stars. A soft wind rustled through the trees and fluttered the leaves on the grapevines. In the distance, an owl called hauntingly.

Bryce took Sarah into his arms, warming her in his embrace.

"It's all over," he whispered. "The harvest, the season, presentation of the new wine. But something else is about to begin. Something even more of a miracle than grapes turning into wine."

His eyes, dark with a desire that had been suppressed too long, bore into hers. "Each time you've come here, I've watched you, hoping to see that you want me as much as I want you."

To her surprise, her voice, when she spoke, was calm and sure. "I want you more than I ever dreamed of wanting anything or anyone."

"That's almost as much as I want you, Sarah."

His lips met hers. The kiss was soft, tender, unhurried. They had all night to discover each other, and he was in no hurry. He was a man who could afford to take his pleasures leisurely, fully. He would enjoy every step of the journey of discovery because he wouldn't be overanxious to reach his destination.

As his lips touched her eyelids, cheeks, forehead, Sarah felt a tiny sigh of happiness escape her. This was what she had wanted from the first moment he walked into her life. This was what she had waited for, yearned for. Long before it was clear in her mind, her heart knew—this was the man she'd looked for her entire life. Whatever else remained to be settled between them, of this much she was certain—tonight they would love each other as neither had ever been loved before.

Keeping one arm around her shoulders, he led her

into his bedroom. He didn't turn on the lamp. The moonlight streaming in through the windows bathed the room in its diaphanous light. With his free hand, Bryce pushed the door closed and Sarah heard the almost inaudible click of the lock.

She slipped off the silk jacket and tossed it onto a chair. Next she bent first one long slender silk-clad leg, then the other, to remove her high-heeled sandals. She was perfectly aware the slits up the sides of her dress revealed a provocative exposure of ankle, calf and thigh.

Sarah heard Bryce's sharp intake of breath. Turning to face him, she stood silhouetted against the moonlit window and opened her arms, inviting... welcoming him.

Before he kissed her, he stood close in her embrace and removed, one by one, the pins that held in place her sleek coiffure. Then he threaded his long fingers through her mane of golden hair, loosening it, freeing it to frame her cheeks.

He covered her face and neck with kisses as he removed first one pearl earring, then the other and slid open the zipper of her dress all the way down her back. When she was naked except for the string of lustrous pearls around her throat, he lifted her as if she was a fragile porcelain figurine, instead of a flesh-and-blood woman whose pulse throbbed with wanting him.

He carried her to the bed. It had been turned down sometime earlier, and now he laid Sarah down on the soft cool sheets.

Slowly his hands caressed her gently sloping shoulders, moved into the curve of her waist, and over the sleekness of her hips. The light of love in his eyes had turned fierce, and Sarah knew his passion was rising. Her own was only tenuously controlled.

At any moment it threatened to break free, throwing off all restraints.

Her earlier hesitancy was now replaced by a womanly confidence. She felt no embarrassment as she lay naked before him. She offered up to him in love her body, as a gift to a god, and was delighted that he was so obviously pleased.

Without being asked, she began to undress him. When he too was naked, her breath caught as she observed the magnificence of his body. He was a powerfully built man with massive shoulders and strong arms. The hardness of his muscles was revealed in the planes of his broad smooth chest. His strength would have been intimidating had Sarah not felt that it was tempered with gentleness.

Looking down at her, he said in a voice hoarse with emotion, "I mean to make you mine completely tonight. I mean to make you forget you were ever loved before."

She smiled in a slow seductive way. "I'm already yours. I have been for a very long time. Long before I even met you." She traced his mouth with her fingertip. "You're my fate."

His mouth softened under her touch as he returned her smile. "Then I'll take what is mine."

He took her first with his lips and his hands, exploring, caressing, kissing. As he touched every inch of her bare skin, she felt as if she were coming alive, as if a fire that had burned down to barely glowing embers was being stirred into flame again. She wanted him to feel everything she was feeling, so she explored him at the same time, arousing him with her fingertips as they touched, glided, descended to the hard maleness of him.

He groaned with pleasure, and her hands continued to move slowly around and over his body. How fine the down was on his arms and legs, how hard the tensed muscles in his thighs as he leaned against her. His touch was as gentle and tender as a summer zephyr caressing her skin. The combination of the hard and soft, the gentle and passionate, was exhilarating. Sarah felt a throbbing, an expectancy. Her whole body was crying out for a fulfillment that she knew only Bryce could give.

And still his hands and lips continued to roam over her body as if searching for something and didn't know whether it was around her breasts, or under them, along her hips, or in the valley between. She knew he could feel her response, could feel the tremors of her body each time his fingertips touched a particularly sensitive area.

"Now," Sarah whispered. She looked up into Bryce's eyes and knew he understood. He moved into her, taking her at first with exquisite tenderness, then growing passion. They moved in marvelous harmony, their excitement rising together. Their bodies were charged with desire, their hearts full to overflowing with love. And when their passion exploded in a burst of ecstasy the very night itself seemed to dissolve around them....

"Sarah?"

"Yes?"

Their voices were whispers in the dark as they lay arms and legs entwined. Sarah's cheek nestled against Bryce's hard chest. She could hear the beating of his heart, calmer than it had been at first, and feel his soft warm breath against her forehead.

"I love you, you know."

"I know."

There was a moment of silence. Then Bryce said, "Well?"

"Well, what?" Sarah asked impishly.

He shook her a little. "Minx! You know what I mean."

She grinned. Then, looking up at him, she said, "I love you too." She rained tiny feather-light kisses across his chest. "Love you…love you…love you."

He stopped her affectionate teasing by pulling her tightly against him.

"Sarah." His voice was sober now. "In case there's any question in your mind, I don't want just an affair. Or living together. I want you to be mine tonight and every night till the end of my life. I want you to marry me."

She'd known this was coming. Bryce wasn't a man to take half measures. The proposal pleased her inordinately. But there were problems, she knew. Problems they hadn't even begun to discuss, let alone resolve.

When she didn't respond, Bryce continued, "Sarah?"

"Hush, love," she whispered. "Let's not talk about it tonight. Let's just…just be together."

He kissed her forehead tenderly and wrapped his arms around her more securely. They fell asleep that way, bound together as if for eternity.

BRYCE SLEPT DEEPLY for a couple of hours, then awoke. He tried to turn over, but something restricted him. Sarah lay in the curve of his arm, her face on his shoulder.

In the predawn light, he watched her sleeping. She was lovely. While her features were not absolutely perfect, they were pleasing. Her cheekbones were quite pronounced, her mouth attractively shaped, and she smiled a lot. Her golden-brown eyes, closed now in sleep, usually reflected a confidence that was reassuring. What he saw came as much from his memory as what he now was able to discern in the pale light. She was not only a beautiful woman, she was a lovely lady.

He liked that she was thoughtful, cautious even.
But not afraid. She'd certainly captivated him that
first day he approached her about his advertising
needs, and she was comfortable enough about herself to admit she could remember being a "hungry"
firm. She thought she could put his campaign together because she knew how to hustle, and she was
still involved with others willing to put a little extra
into their work.

Most of all, what he admired about her was her
sense of honor. Not only was she a lady, in the truest
sense of the word, she was also a gentleman. Bryce
smiled as he thought how pleased she'd be with his
evaluation. But she had been, she didn't come to him
until she felt comfortable to do so.

He didn't *actually* place his hand on her to follow
the curve of her small waist, slim hip, and down the
long slender thigh she'd enjoyed revealing in her
deliberately provocative teasing last night, but he
did in fantasy. And to his imagined touch, her skin
was fine-textured and silken smooth. Her legs were
beautifully proportioned and shaped. Lustrous silk-
stockinged legs, presented one at a time through the
parted white silk so that the three-inch heeled straps
of black could be unbuckled and dropped carelessly
on the floor. That had been a delightful number she
had done on him. He'd sensed in that first kiss—the
very first one after the Mozart concert, that she was
a woman of considerable passion. She was that. And
more. Last night he'd been excited by her seductive
posing, but now—there was time to remember and
appreciate her intent. To pleasure him.... Just thinking about it gave him pleasure again. And warmed
him. And excited him.

Bryce felt a joining of different facets of himself.
Lying next to this woman who was that other half of
him, the half he'd been searching for. It was as if, all

at once, he himself came into focus. It was an interesting collection of bits and pieces that had finally dropped into place when he thought about Sarah's provocative sandal-removing routine. She'd been free enough—trusting enough to be deliberately sensual. She'd received as much stimulation and excitement from knowing he found her beautiful as he had from watching her. Together they would have a tremendous potential for loving.

Bryce had loved Melissa for a short time when he was a very young man. Beautiful, voluptuous, sophisticated, Melissa had been the personification of love. But he knew Melissa had not betrayed him, he had only himself to blame. His grandfather, his father, even Thaddeus, had suggested that he take a little more time to decide. But it had been lonely at Madrona for too long. Four men, alone. After years of three men and one boy, he thought he knew what he wanted. And he thought it was Melissa.

Looking at Sarah now, her long lashes a fragile feathering curve on the ivory smoothness of her skin, he saw the dark tinge of fatigue smudging half-circles beneath her eyes. She'd had strong family connections. She'd been taught to love. By example.

Melissa, on the other hand, did not have a family. Only a widowed mother, barely seventeen years older than her daughter. Melissa had commented once that had her mother not been a widow, she'd certainly have been the gay divorcée.

Bright, unchallenged, practically abandoned, Melissa had grown up in a succession of expensive boarding schools. After the first year of marriage, when the discontent had set in, Bryce often wondered what it was about him that had attracted Melissa. And what might have happened if she'd gotten pregnant immediately. Would that just have completed, for her, the "playing house" game?

Oh, he remembered, they'd had a fantastic sex life that first couple of years. But once Adam made his appearance, and still she pursued the challenge of archaeology—advancing her degrees, testing her knowledge on short digs—their relationship grew cool, then cold, and after she accepted the African dig, bitter.

Bryce had grown up with tender care, but it was lonely without that loving woman who'd been his mother. He had a deep regret that Adam really never knew that kind of feminine nurturing either. Bryce knew he'd betrayed himself. And vowed not to betray Adam who was already wary. Wariness was born of fear.

Bryce understood that. When he'd lost his mother, he'd been terrified that he'd lose his father as well. Luis became such a stranger. Work became his therapy and, as a result, there were several award-winning Benedict houses scattered throughout northern California.

Thaddeus had been there, but while he'd been caring, he wasn't as seasoned as he was now. It had been his grandfather, widowed too, but come to terms with it, who'd nurtured him, taking him into the harvest. And instilling in him, that year, the promise of the good life, tied to the land. He wished Adam had a grandfather such as he had had.

Sarah stirred and Bryce watched her, hoping she'd open her eyes. But she sighed, and then her breathing regained its even tempo and the string of pearls she wore gleamed softly.

There was something about her that emanated from deep within, centered to those same traditions he himself felt anchored to. That was why he told

her he wanted to marry her. She was the only
woman he had wanted to make his wife.

There'd been other ladies who had tried to charm
Adam, win Adam, beguile the father and the boy.
Sometimes it had been amusing, Adam's aloofness.

No one except this lady met with any success.
Was it because she didn't try, that she succeeded?
She had taken her own time to come to this rela-
tionship.

Two months, he reflected, concentrating again on
Sarah. No, ten weeks. From zero to here. And suddenly, the eroticism that he'd been able to sublimate
caused his hand to disobey his brain and cup the
yielding fullness of her breast. Hell, he thought, his
immediate arousal now a threat to Sarah's sleep.

He knew that if he didn't get out of bed at once, he
was going to make love to her before she had a
chance to wake up. He felt her response against his
palm.

"Damn," he breathed, and withdrawing his arm
from beneath her shoulders, turned over and swung
his legs to the floor.

Sarah felt that welcomed hand. In the world of
half sleep, she was dreamily conscious of Bryce's
coming awake. As his senses registered her presence,
his body responded. All along the length of their
touching, she was fully aware of his arousal. Her
breast, lying against his heart, had felt the change
from a slow steady beat to a faster cadence. The
muscles in his arm, clasping her, flexed involuntarily. The sound of his breathing changed from a mea-
sured to an irregular rhythm.

And her quickening kept pace with his.

She lay there warmly intoxicated by the memory
of last night's lovemaking, bathed in a luxuriant
sensuality. She had felt free to say "I love you" while
making love . . . and receiving him in his total com-

mitment to loving her had been a powerful aphro-
disiac.

Her senses collected now, she was about to cover
his hand cupping her responding breast, when she
heard him refuse his desire.

His consideration was misplaced. Granted she'd
had little sleep. But she could sleep another day.
Now she wanted to love him and have him love her.

Deliberately she remained in that drowsily voluptuous state of readiness. She did not turn to speak to
him, but she heard him quietly open the wardrobe
and remove...a robe probably, since immediately
she heard the smooth gliding of the glass doors that
opened onto his private balcony.

He'll be back, she told herself and stretched lan-
guidly, as sensuously aware of her own sexuality as
she was of his. *Come back, darling. You went away just
one second too soon.*

She waited a minute or two, then threw off the
covers and got up. There was a dark red dressing
gown hanging in his wardrobe. She slipped it on,
not bothering to tie the sash. It smelled of silk...and
him.

The door slid open without a sound. Bryce was
standing at the railing of the balcony, looking east.
He didn't realize she was there until she slipped her
arms around him and laid her cheek against his
shoulder.

Immediately he overlaid her hands with his, holding her close against him, and shifted slightly so that
Sarah's view would be the same as his...the eastern
slopes at dawn.

They did not speak, but stood in silence. Then
Sarah felt a pressure from Bryce's hand, signaling as
the first crack appeared in the grayness. Then that
split became an ever-widening streak along the horizon as the sun, big and red and shimmering, began

to edge over the dark silhouette of the mountain's crest.

Sarah saw the splendor of the sunrise showering red and gold over the trees, hillsides, rows of vineyards. The entire world was washed with that dazzling brightness. Surely, she thought, the Greeks were right. Apollo is driving the sun chariot through the sky. It was a sign, this beautiful radiance, marking the close of a marvelous night and the beginning of a wonderful new day.

"My grandfather," Bryce said in a hushed voice, "used to talk about all this land as if it were a living thing. He'd say, for some, land is something you buy, sell, trade. A commodity. A piece of merchandise. But for him, the land was to be owned, worked, treasured."

Listening to him, Sarah realized he was telling her something important about himself. He'd already told her he felt about Madrona the way his grandfather had. And that he never wanted to be anywhere but here.

She could understand that. Her grandfather felt that way about his land. Interesting, how those two old men from widely distanced places spoke almost identical words.

Standing there beside Bryce as he surveyed what was now his, he continued to repeat some of the things he'd already told her. How his grandfather had begun as a cooper working for other vineyardists. Acquiring land as he was able, until he had all of this. Then he brought his bride here, built his home, reared his son. And died here.

"That year he died, we were out walking after harvest and he stopped and told me that I must care for this land. That it would be mine after my father left it to my *husbandry*. Granddad used strong, old-fashioned words. He didn't allow for any misinter-

pretation. I was to improve it and protect it for
Adam. And Adam for his son...." Then, almost as if
talking to himself, he drew a deep breath and said
proudly, "It *is* beautiful land. And the harvest is going to be bountiful."

Bountiful, Sarah thought, was also an old-fashioned
word that left no doubt as to its meaning. She felt
Bryce's tension ease. The homage paid, she wondered.

He pulled her around to face him.

"Good morning," she said, raising her face to look
at him, noting his tousled silky brown hair.

"I love you." His voice was rich and husky. "I
watched you sleeping and decided that if I didn't get
up, I'd have to wake you up." He smiled teasingly at
her and lifted one eyebrow suggestively, making
sure that his meaning was clear.

Her smile was deliberately enticing. "I'm awake
now."

Reaching inside the dressing gown, he ran his
hands across her bare back and drew her to him. At
first his kiss was tender, then it grew passionate.
Against her mouth, he whispered, "Since you are,
let's go back to bed."

As they stepped inside the room, Bryce said,
"You're even more beautiful in the daylight than
you were in the moonlight. And that's saying something."

He shed his robe and then slid the dark red silk off
her smooth white shoulders. "Let's get properly un-
dressed," he invited.

"Let's," she whispered, love and desire commingling in her glowing brown eyes as was gold and
green and brown in his.

Slowly and deliberately she lifted her hands to
unclasp the tiny fastener on the string of gleaming
lustrous pearls. Then, holding them between her

thumb and finger, she pulled them from around her neck and extended her arm to its full length. Never releasing him with her eyes, she dropped the pearls onto the carpet beside one of the black high-heeled sandals.

14

WHEN SARAH AWOKE THE SECOND TIME, the drapes were drawn and the room was dark. The digital clock on the nightstand read 10:32...10:33.

Good heavens. She'd really slept late. Even before turning her head toward where Bryce had lain, she knew she was alone.

As she raised her arms above her head in a luxuriant stretch, she inhaled deeply and encountered the sweet fragrance of a rose. Quickly she turned her head. There on the edge of her pillow was a velvety red rose. She had suggested red roses for the buffet's centerpiece.

She held the rose up to admire its beauty and fragrance, and most of all its message. Lucky you, Sarah, she told herself, lucky, lucky you.

Her overnight bag was sitting where she couldn't help but see it. She'd mentioned that she'd brought one, but had left it in her car. Bryce had thoughtfully retrieved it for her.

She showered and dressed in her favorite pair of pleated pants. Eggshell colored, heavy shantung. And a nubby sweater of the same soft shading, with tracery of pointillé work forming the yoke and accenting the boat neckline. Sarah pushed up the long sleeves to just below her elbows and stepped into a pair of low-heeled camel pumps.

She brushed her hair until it fell in a shining sheath, touched the glass stopper of Joy behind each ear and at the hollow of her throat, and with a self-satisfied smile, clipped on her pearl earrings. Last, but certainly not least, she picked up the string of pearls Bryce obviously had retrieved from the carpet and fastened them around her neck. Remembering—she gave her mirrored reflection a wink and sighed happily.

Her clothes, which she had so carelessly and joyfully abandoned last night, were no longer strewn about. The silk dress and jacket were hanging on a padded hanger. The sandals were placed neatly side by side under the chair upon which lay the gossamer wisps of lace underwear and silk stockings.

After making up the bed, she quickly packed the clothes into her bag. Then, stopping to open the drapes, she left the room.

SARAH SAT AT A SMALL TABLE on the redwood deck looking at the vineyards. The vines here were no longer heavy with fruit. She knew there were still slow-ripening grapes in the coolest part of the vineyard, but most of the harvest was gathered. Gathered... where had that word come from? She'd enjoyed Bryce's use of "bountiful" when he spoke of the harvest. "Gathering in the Sheaves" was an old hymn she'd heard every summer when she visited the farm. At least, that was the way papa sang it, much to grandmother's dismay. "It's 'Bringing in the Sheaves,'" she would insist.

Papa liked the sound of "gathering" better. "You sow and you reap and you gather in the harvest," he had said.

Grandmother never won, even when she tried for the final word. "You could think gathering and sing bringing like everyone else." He always bested her. But with love—a quick hug and an affectionate peck on her cheek.

Looking out over the beautiful countryside, Sarah

considered how alike she and Bryce seemed to be. Families, values, appreciation of attitudes and ideals, intrinsic things. Just thinking about him and the happiness she felt made her want to fling wide her arms and embrace the world. Falling in love was indeed wonderful.

Of course, there were some serious considerations to be resolved. But as another song promised, love will find the way.

All they needed was time. Time now to enjoy this period of joyful discovery. And what a marvelous exotic journey of exploration last night and this morning had been. Sarah had thought she knew herself. But last night she'd learned something that she'd previously only suspected. She was capable of an enjoyment...a sensuality...a response that was wonderful to discover. Bryce had taken her on this exotic erotic journey. She had trusted him enough to let down the bars, open the gates, forget the self-imposed boundaries of how much to give and how far to go. And he was the only one who'd ever seen that particularly uninhibited Sarah Montgomery.

Which wasn't to say that her relationship with John had been stilted, unsatisfying, certainly not circumspect. John had been a thoughtful, considerate lover. It was just that because John held back his commitment, even to fidelity, she'd always withheld that part of her that showed what she was really like.

It is because I feel safe with Bryce, she told herself.

An old proverb, "Trust in God, but tie your camel," flashed into her mind. She wanted to laugh aloud with the sheer exuberance of loving him. She was "home." Safe.

"Good morning."

Sarah looked up into Thaddeus's bright friendly smile. He carried a tray of coffee.

"Good morning, yourself. Oh, thank you. I was just coming to find a cup of coffee."

"It was on the counter in the kitchen. I always leave it there for Bryce. He likes to have a cup before going to the winery. Then he returns and has breakfast with Adam. Is he at the winery now?"

"I suppose. I was still sleeping...."

She stopped, although she really did not feel awkward talking to Thaddeus. He surely knew she had spent the night in Bryce's bedroom and not the guest room. She wondered if she'd be this comfortable when Adam appeared.

"You look very happy this morning, Sarah, if I may say so."

"You may say so. It was a heavenly party last night, wasn't it? And Bryce's Recherché is launched."

"And successfully. Luis would have been pleased about that." Thaddeus sipped his coffee, then replaced the cup to its saucer and leaned back comfortably in his chair. He stretched out his legs, crossed them at the ankles and tilted his face to the sunshine. "Adam been to see you yet?"

"No. Is he up?"

"Yes, and already fed. He's been waiting for you to get up. He was delighted to see your car still here."

"Oh." That meant that he probably knew where she'd slept. "I hope the guest-room door was discreetly closed," she said.

"It was. You've nothing to be ashamed of, Sarah. Adam will be very happy to see you."

"I think you're probably right. I like him very much and I think he's beginning to like me. Especially since I took him a plate of your most exotic hors d'oeuvres last night, after I caught him raiding the buffet table."

"Yes, he told me." Thaddeus sat up straight in his

chair and looked directly at her. "He more than likes you...Sarah. He's beginning to trust you. At first, you know, he was afraid to show his feelings. You might not have come back."

He poured more coffee for both of them, then asked, "Is there a problem? Is that a pensive look I see?"

She answered slowly. "Bryce asked me to marry him."

"But why should that make you pensive? I thought you looked like a lady in love."

"I am. In love, I mean. But it's all very new."

"I see."

He *did* see, she knew. He understood the hesitation in her voice. He was silent for a long moment. Finally he responded, "That was a very big step for him to take. It wasn't difficult for him to lose Melissa. Love was long gone from that situation. But it was difficult for him to have Adam lose his mother. When a career separates a woman from her child it becomes a very intimidating subject. He's come a long way. Falling in love with you, being willing to risk being hurt again. Although I suspect his falling in love with you is entirely different than when he fell in love that very first time."

Determined that nothing was going to dull the bright edge of this wonderful day, Sarah replied, "Well, he certainly knew I was a career woman before he asked me to marry him." And, she told herself, he certainly knew where her office was located. Shari and Art were combining their talents to give themselves a fuller, richer life. She and Bryce could too. They would just have to take time to resolve the logistics of their respective careers, she decided. And to define their separate and mutual responsibilities.

She felt no fear, no apprehension. When she'd accepted his silent invitation... command... request... last night as his head dealt with the wine critic and his heart with her, she'd acknowledged that she loved him. And more, she trusted him. "We can work it all out. I love him. He loves me."

"Well," Thaddeus said, "if it isn't that simple, it ought to be. Certainly many women combine marriage, children and careers. You and Bryce love each other in a way that happens only rarely. And even more importantly, you're *right* for each other. Many people, perhaps most, never find that one person who is absolutely right for them. It happened to me, but I was foolish enough to let it go."

He was silent for a moment, then continued, "Sometimes to make something work, you have to fight for it. Even compromise for it." He grinned at her, adding, "I'll do my part. If it pleases you, I'll be happy to continue as general factotum, as Bryce terms it. You won't have to devote yourself to housework and cooking unless you want to."

"Oh, Thaddeus, I never considered the possibility of anything else. I thought you came with the territory. Like Adam."

He smiled happily. "Well, thank you. I'm relieved to hear you feel that way."

Just then Bryce appeared with a bright-eyed Adam at his side.

"Look who I found," he said.

"Sarah! I've been waiting for you," Adam exclaimed joyfully.

"Good morning, I'm happy to see you."

Running up to her, he gave her a big hug. The sheer impulsiveness of the loving gesture warmed Sarah's heart. Her eyes met Bryce's and she felt a lump in her throat. They were going to be a family, she thought.

"I'd better get to work on breakfast," Thaddeus

announced, rising and setting down his coffee cup. Looking at Adam, he asked, "Want to help crack the eggs?"

"This is lunch. I had breakfast. But I like eggs for lunch!" he responded enthusiastically and raced ahead of Thaddeus toward the kitchen.

When Bryce and Sarah were alone, he sat down beside her. For a moment, he simply looked at her. She met his gaze, saying nothing. All she felt for him was in her eyes.

Finally, he said, "You belong here. With us. We all want you to stay forever."

"I know." Her voice was a whisper.

"Do you want to stay?"

"You know I do."

He caught something, a note of hesitancy, in her voice, that made his smile waver. "But...."

"But...oh darling, I was just telling Thaddeus, we can work out all the logistics. But you know we've both been through relationships that didn't work. It's important to be careful the second time around."

He smiled. Then he leaned over to kiss her lips tenderly. "The last thing in the world I feel like being right now is careful. I want you, Sarah. And you want me."

"That's what I told Thaddeus. But between you and me, it isn't that simple, is it? Oh, Bryce, we haven't talked about my business, your business, how on earth we're going to handle Adam—"

"Adam loves you. And so do I."

She felt her heart leap at the sound of those beautiful words. He loved her. And she loved him. Oh, how she loved him.

He reached out to stroke her cheek lightly. "Sarah, the French have a phrase that sums it up—'friend of the heart.' I want to be your friend of the heart, to cherish you, care for you, share my life with you."

"Oh, Bryce, that's what I want too!" she said, hugging him tightly.

As they clung to each other, Sarah thought she'd never known she could be this happy. Whatever they had to work out, they could.

Adam came running to the door. "Thaddeus says lunch's ready."

AFTER LUNCH, THADDEUS PERSUADED a reluctant Adam that a short siesta would do them both a world of good.

In the living room, seated close beside each other on the sofa, Bryce kissed Sarah softly on her cheek and asked, "How about you? Would you like a siesta?"

"What I might like and what I intend to do are two very different things." Placing her hand on his, she smiled. "Thank you, but I really must decline your kind invitation."

"If you'd give me a moment in private, I might change your mind."

"You might indeed. That's why I'm not giving you that moment." She brushed his lips with hers, then said, "I must be getting back. I have a million things to do tomorrow. I'm a bit behind in my work. Something else has been occupying my interest. I just remembered I have several other clients. And Art and Shari made an appointment for next week. Isn't that great? Their project sounds like a real winner."

Sarah told him that because of the success of the Recherché campaign, she'd been offered an important new account. A large chain of restaurants, with its headquarters in San Francisco, wanted her to devise an ad campaign to publicize a major redecorating job it had done. This was the biggest account she'd ever been offered—bigger even than Recherché. It would mean a quantum leap for her agency, thrusting it into the big time. "Isn't that thrilling?" she finished. "It's incredible that they passed over all the major agencies and came to *me*."

Bryce smiled affectionately. "I don't think it's incredible. Shows good taste on their part."

He took her in his arms and hugged her tightly. "You're brilliant and beautiful and *mine*."

He kissed her deeply.

When she finally came up from the passionate depths of that kiss, she responded huskily, "I am certainly yours."

"I am proud of you, Sarah. But no more talk about business today. I won't mention wine and you don't mention advertising. There's something much more important than either of those things to discuss."

"And what's that?" she asked with an impish grin.

"Our wedding. I don't care how you want to handle it, as long as you don't insist on a long engagement. Well, I guess I should add that perhaps Adam can be the ring bearer. And Thaddeus my best man."

"Perfect." She added with a slight hesitation, "Bryce—do you mind if we have the wedding in Faribault? That way, all my family and old friends can attend."

"Of course I don't mind. I expected you to feel that way, in fact. We'll be married, but we will have to come right back. Honeymoon after December when I have some slack time. Do you have a preference—the Caribbean, Europe, Mexico?"

She threw her arms around his neck and turned up her face to brush her lips teasingly across his. "I don't care *where* we go. I expect we'll spend most of our time in a hotel room, anyway."

Her brown eyes glinted with the glowing embers of a fire that Bryce could easily stir into a blazing inferno. As he looked down at her, he responded in a voice grown suddenly husky with passion, "I expect you're right."

They kissed again, long and slow and deep. When they finally parted, Sarah whispered, "I think I'd better go before we reach the point of no return."

"I think I've already reached it," Bryce replied, nuzzling her neck, then biting it playfully. "How about that siesta now, *señorita?*"

Laughing, Sarah pulled away. "No way, *señor*. I have to make tracks back to the city."

Bryce sighed. "Woman, you're hard to convince." Releasing her, he relaxed and continued, "So, when would you like to be married? I don't have anything planned next weekend."

She chortled. "Oh no you don't. I'm going to wear my mother's wedding gown and that will take some fitting. We have to hire a caterer and mail invitations. And arrange for flowers. Red carnations will look nice at Christmastime, don't you think?"

Startled, Bryce said, "Christmas? Is that when you had in mind?"

"Well... yes. With this new account, there's no way I can take the time to go back to Faribault until then."

"Sarah, this is just October."

"The *end* of October. We're only talking about two months, really."

"Two months is a long time. I want you in my house, in my bed, in my life, before then."

His tone had grown peremptory, just as she'd remembered it from the early days of their relationship.

Her mellow feeling of peace and happiness disappeared. Forcing herself to remain calm, she explained carefully, "Bryce, this is a big job. I can't take two weeks off in the middle of it to get married. I

can't take even a week, right now. I had already put
them on hold until I finished everything for Recherché."

"And what if another big job comes along between now and Christmas? Will you put the wedding off again?"

Be calm, Sarah told herself. *Bryce is overreacting.
Don't do the same.*

"Once we set a date," she said quietly, "I won't
put the wedding off. You know I'm as anxious as
you are. I'll turn down jobs before I'll change the
date. But I need this time now for the job and planning the wedding. It's important, can't you understand?"

He hesitated, then sighed and admitted reluctantly, "I suppose what's worrying me isn't so much
what's happening right now as what it means for
the future."

"You mean, will I put my work before you always?"

The question took on a life of its own. Sarah
watched a wariness come over his countenance and,
just like that first time when they'd lunched at
Doro's, his hazel eyes betrayed the distrust he suddenly experienced. That strange commingling of
gold to green to brown darkened his eyes. And not
with passion as they had done last night and this
morning.

He waited. He hadn't moved out of his relaxed
position, but Sarah felt the tension build in the air
between them.

"You mean," she repeated, "will I put my work
before you always?"

A small knot of fear deep inside her began to form,
and with every breath she drew, that knot grew.
"Friend of the heart" had a nice ring to it. But did it
have any truth, she wondered.

There was a hard set now to his features, and no golden highlights dancing in those expressive eyes.

She thought of last night, their lovemaking in the moonlight...and in that magic red wash of dawn. She thought of her fulfillment, made possible, she knew, by her trust to offer, demand, receive. No holding back with this man, all or nothing.

"Bryce, darling," she tried again, "I want to be married at home. With the blessing of my family. That is very important to me. I will trust you and the love I know we feel for each other to work out all our problems. My career, your career, whatever else might come up." She paused and took a deep breath. "But you must trust me also." Looking him straight in the eye she asked, "Are you afraid that I'll always put my work before you?"

He gazed at her soberly. "Yes."

"And you can't trust me not to let that happen?" When he didn't answer immediately, she realized what was really on his mind. "You think I'll be like Melissa, don't you?"

"I didn't say that," he replied quietly.

"But you're thinking it." Suddenly that knot of fear dissolved and in its place was disappointment and rage. "Bryce, admit it. You think I'll be like Melissa."

"I did *not* say that." His voice rose in its insistence.

She turned away from him, wondering how to make her escape.

"Sarah...."

Before she could answer, the telephone began its insistent pealing. After several rings, Bryce rose and walked to the kitchen to answer it.

Sarah sat waiting, scarcely breathing, she was so astounded at the turn of this conversation. When Bryce came into the room, she looked up.

"Sarah, I'm terribly sorry, but something's come

up at the winery and I've got to go. I'll be back as soon as I can. We've got to finish...please wait for me."

She didn't speak, but merely nodded. As soon as he left the room, she hurried to pick up her overnight bag. She scribbled a hasty note to Adam and Thaddeus and left it on the kitchen counter.

You're a nice girl, Sarah Montgomery, she told herself. Remembering to write a thank-you note at a time like this.

SARAH DROVE QUICKLY PAST THE WINERY, grateful that if Bryce saw her red car going past, she didn't see him. She cut east across to the Oakville Road and drove up to the crest of the Mayacamus Range. It had been August when she'd been here before, early in her involvement with Recherché and Bryce Benedict. When she reached the familiar picnic spot with its panoramic view, she pulled off the road, stopped the car and set the emergency brake. She sat utterly still, her hands folded in her lap.

It was a golden Indian-summer afternoon. The sky was bright blue, and sunlight transformed a cluster of autumn-yellow aspen trees into a shifting lustrous collage. With each gentle breeze that drifted across the mountaintop, the leaves of the trees danced into different patterns, one golden leaf interchanging with another. Then, the next breath of wind would spin them into anther set, and with different partners.

Sarah observed their ballet, watched the delicate ones that lost their tenuous hold to the branches fall, twisting and turning to the ground. Some stayed where they fell, caught in the dry grass, but a few hardy ones followed the wind and pirouetted across the rise.

She gazed out across the broad valley and bordering hillside. Rich reds and yellows checkerboarded a green background, the vineyards turning now in their season's finale. The areas of the mountainsides not in vines were covered with evergreens intermittently splashed with the yellow of aspen and the red-orange of the oaks and maples. One cold rain and this would be even more beautiful, all the vines coming into even fuller color. The promise of blazing flamboyancy was there.

The promise, she thought, and suddenly felt totally bereft. Her disconsolation came from disappointment in Bryce, she told herself. Then, being honest, acknowledged that it came also from chagrin at her own boldness. Remembering her behavior with him last night and again at dawn, she knew she'd never felt so in concert with another. Always...always she'd held back that last vestige of self-control. Never before been willing to trust enough to let go completely and be literally transported. Before last night, rapture was something she'd only read about.

She thought again of the heights—the ecstasy— his lovemaking had brought her to. She closed her eyes and felt his soft mouth on hers. She'd trusted in the promise of love.

Once again she watched the leaves twirling to the tempo of the wind. Dancing with first one partner, then another. A different dance with a different partner. That's what she had done. She'd chosen to change partners and to dance with Bryce.

Oh, Bryce, she thought, *I was audacious with you. A bold partner for you.*

For the first time she had trusted love enough to initiate...to play the temptress. How boldly she'd smiled into his eyes as she'd unclasped the string of pearls so that she would be totally nude...and reveled in his obvious desire.

A strong gust of wind blew through the trees and

for a few moments the top branches of the aspens swayed back and forth to the increased force. The ballet of the leaves changed tempo. The act of love-making was like a dance, Sarah reflected. Arms and legs entwine, bodies arch and press, thrust and yield. First one dancer seduces with sensuous touches of skin upon skin, excites with kisses that are soft and tender, then hard and demanding—finally deep and rewarding.

All the while the partners listen and respond to the music of passion. And as the rhythm accelerates, the flame burns hotter and brighter until the fire consumes the desire. And then the heart is satisfied.

Her heart had been strangely disquieted from that first evening at Madrona, the evening they'd listened to the Mozart, until last night. Everything about her life changed after that first kiss in the moonlight. She'd taken time to come to terms with the passion he aroused in her—to make sure that there was true reciprocity in their desire for each other.

Until last night, she had not yielded to him. Not until she was comfortable with her decision to change partners had she acceded. Then, she'd not only yielded, she'd joyously released all the passion she'd never before shared.

From that first mid-August meeting with Bryce Benedict, she'd walked that dizzying tightrope of seduction. Then last night, she'd believed the promise. But just like the dancing leaves caught in the wind, she too had fallen. *Oh, Bryce,* her heart cried, *were we not dancing to the same music?*

Her eyes misted with tears and the scene blurred. She felt uncomfortable—naked, somehow shame-fully exposed in her naïveté. Her discomfort became a hurting throbbing pain.

The rage and disappointment that had begun as

fear flooded over her. All this beauty is incongruous, she thought. The land should be bleak, the vines shriveled. The promise of the harvest, the wine, unfulfilled. Like the promise of Bryce's love.... Last night and this morning was all a lie.

Leaning her arms on the steering wheel, Sarah cradled her face and wept bitterly as she hadn't wept for years and years.

"She left." Thaddeus's expression and tone were carefully neutral.

"What?" Bryce was stunned. He went on quickly, "Did she say anything?"

"No. She just left a note indicating she had to get back to the city."

For a moment, Bryce simply stood in the living room, saying nothing. Watching him, Thaddeus's expression clouded over with concern.

"Bryce...if you want to talk about it...."

"Thanks, Thaddeus. But I think I'll just go into my study for a while. I've got some thinking to do."

"I understand. I'll keep Adam occupied."

In his study, Bryce leaned back in the tall leather chair and fiddled absently with a pencil. Now that the first shock was over, he wasn't surprised Sarah had left. When they had been arguing, part of him was aware of the fact that he was hurting her deeply. But he ignored that awareness. And now....

She should have stayed, he insisted angrily to himself. Running away while his back was turned was cowardly.

Ah, but who's the real coward, a voice inside him asked. Is it Sarah—who was ready to risk everything, trusting that he would love her enough to make it work? Or was it he, who couldn't bring himself to entirely trust what she felt for him?

The answer was obvious.

He'd been unbelievably harsh in comparing her to Melissa. She *wasn't* Melissa. Sarah was a sensitive, caring, compassionate woman, with a profound ability to love and be loved. She could give more than Bryce ever thought a woman could give, and accept everything Bryce and Adam had to offer in return.

And he had hurt her, perhaps irreparably.

"Damn!" he muttered, slamming one tightly balled fist down on the desk.

Sarah...she'd come into his life when he'd almost stopped hoping to ever find real love. She made his world seem new and exciting again. She filled the emptiness with her warm caring presence. And gave herself to him as he knew she'd never given herself to any man.

And now it was all over, all of that love was lost simply because he didn't have the courage to trust what she felt for him.

What a fool I've been, he thought, shaking his head. From the first moment he'd realized that he loved her, he'd been afraid—afraid the same thing would happen that happened in his marriage. *I must trust her love for me and for Adam,* he silently concluded. He'd have to let her be what she needed to be. And hope that whatever else her life might involve, Adam and he would always be at the center of it.

All right, so I've been a fool, he told himself sternly. *But I don't have to go on being one.*

Rising, he strode out of the study and into the living room. Thaddeus sat there, reading a book to Adam. When Bryce came in, both Thaddeus and Adam looked up at him.

"I'm going into the city," Bryce announced.

Thaddeus smiled and Adam looked surprised.

"When will you be back, dad?" Adam asked. "Can I come too?"

"I'm not sure when I'll be back. Certainly no later than tomorrow. And, no, you can't come with me this time. Next time, I promise."

Thaddeus said, "Don't worry about hurrying back. Adam and I will be just fine."

Meeting his look Bryce responded, "Wish me luck."

"I do. All the luck in the world."

SARAH'S PHONE WAS RINGING when she entered her apartment. Without thinking, she picked it up and said, "Hello."

Then she panicked. What if it was Bryce? She didn't want to talk with him. There was nothing more to be said.

But it was only her mother wanting to ask how the party went and was the wine a success. Sarah forced herself to distance her pain, and chatted with her mother for a few minutes. Then, telling a small white lie, said she had to hurry and dress for dinner.

She'd hardly replaced the receiver when the phone rang again. This time she was more cautious. She let it ring nine times before she answered it. If it should be Bryce, she told herself, she might as well terminate this now as later. She couldn't live her life afraid to answer the telephone.

"Hello, Sarah. This is papa."

"Oh, papa...." She was going to have a hard time with this call. She'd never been successful hiding her feelings from this man. She'd been his first grandchild, his only one for two years, and during that time they had bonded in a very special way.

"I just called to ask if *now* you're rich and famous?" he teased. "The wine was a success?"

She tried her best to sound cheerful and bright as they talked about the party, the wine, her new opportunities, but finally he interrupted her in mid-sentence.

"Sarah, child...is something wrong?"

"No." What was wrong was nothing she could tell papa.

"Well," he said, releasing her, "I was watching our sunset a little while ago and thinking about harvest...and how now you're involved in a harvest. Remember, honey, sometimes harvest is so much work. There's so much ridin' on the need for a good crop, people can get out of sorts."

He understood. Even without her telling him, he knew she was having a difficult time today. She thanked him for his call, told him she would telephone him in a few days and said, "Goodbye, papa. I love you."

"I love you too, child. And remember, always give the extra measure." He hung up before anything more could be said.

Not wanting to risk another phone call, Sarah picked up a sweater and quickly left her apartment. Without even thinking about where to walk, she turned toward the Filbert Steps.

When she reached the bench, she rubbed her fingers over the plaque. *You're right,* she said silently, *we're not in Kansas anymore. And we're certainly not in the Valley of the Moon.*

Then she heard papa saying...always give the extra measure.

Hadn't she? Was the harvest more stressful than she perceived? Bryce seemed the epitome of self-confidence. When she first met him, she'd have used a stronger word to describe him.

The sun was setting and bringing an end to this day. For some reason, she couldn't stop thinking about what papa had understood and replied to. She'd told Bryce about that wheat crop of papa's that had been destroyed just before they were to harvest. It had been a late afternoon, like this. Sarah remembered telling papa that the grain looked like a golden ocean with the summer breeze blowing through it. For as many miles as she could see, the grain swayed in undulating waves.

Her grandfather and his friend had stood beside her talking seriously about how a miscalculation of just a day or two could mean a poor grade of wheat and low market prices. It was July and the wheat was waist high, the heads ripened to a rich golden hue.

The two men had talked about educated guesses. One guess, if correct, and papa could receive a high price per bushel. But even if he began harvest at the grain's peak of ripeness, he was still at nature's mercy.

Kuan Yin hadn't smiled on papa.

What Sarah thought about now as she sat sorting out her own feelings of betrayal and disappointment was what her grandfather had said to her the following day when she'd asked him what would he do now that the crop was destroyed.

"When it's time, I'll plant more wheat. That's what a wheat farmer does." He'd talked of other things, then ended by saying that whether you're a farmer or a lovely girl like herself, there are good times and bad times. Sometimes you reap a bountiful harvest. And sometimes you have to replant a failed crop. Then he'd said, "But always give the extra measure."

And Sarah, remembering those words, felt the hurt and anger of the quarrel leave her. She and Bryce did love each other. She should have stayed and worked their way through their misunderstanding. She should have given that extra measure.

She would go home right now and call him. Standing up, she turned to climb the steps.

Bryce was there, coming down, so close she could see the love shining in his eyes. For a second she thought her heart would stop. Then, knowing why he had come, she drew a deep breath and felt again its rhythmic cadence.

When he reached the bench, he gestured with his hand for her to sit down. He sat beside her and took her in his arms. He didn't speak, nor did she. He simply held her, gently...tenderly...as he had that day at Wolf House when he told her that someday he wouldn't let her run away from what was between them.

And he sighed, again as he had that day, a deep, deep sigh. Then he shifted so that her head rested upon his shoulder, and asked, "How about Thanksgiving?"

She nodded. She didn't know how she would manage, but this was what it was all about. Compromise.

"Tell me about your mother's wedding gown. Will it require a train carrier? Does its wearing demand a six bridesmaids and six groomsmen spectacular?"

"No. It's a beautifully simple dress. My mother made it for her own wedding. She's very creative."

"When you were a little girl playing bride, did you get to wear it?"

"Heavens, no. But my mother used to let my sister and me see it."

"Did you ever consider before that you'd like to wear it?" he asked, looking down at her.

"No," she said. "I've never gotten this close before."

"Close? Far! Thanksgiving is a long time away. Tell me about the dress."

"It's ivory satin. The design is very simple. The

beauty of the dress is in its flow, its cut, the way it molds. I always meant to walk down the aisle of our church on my father's arm, preceded by my sister, knowing my mother had been seated by my brother in her place...and the rest of family there. And always, I meant to be wearing that gown."

"What time of day is this wedding taking place?" he asked, now tilting her face to look directly at her.

"It's late afternoon...and the sun is shining through the tall windows of the church." She was whispering now, seeing the love in his eyes, knowing he saw the same in hers.

Bryce picked up her story. "Instead of the usual bridal bouquet, the bride carries a small ivory-bound bible." He paused, then continued, "It had been the bridegroom's mother's. Ask me about the flowers," he said.

"How is the church decorated?"

"With stands of ivory candles and huge baskets of bronze chrysanthemums."

Lifting her lips to his, she smiled and said, "Didn't you hear the pastor? He said you may kiss the bride."

And there on the "Kansas" bench, high on Telegraph Hill, as the setting sun turned golden the windows of the city by the Golden Gate, he kissed her.

And Sarah knew that, indeed, that magnetic needle deep within had pointed her north to Bryce. And love.